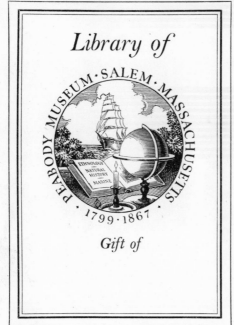

FEWER AND BETTER BABIES

BIRTH CONTROL

OR

THE LIMITATION OF OFFSPRING BY PREVENCEPTION

BY

WILLIAM J. ROBINSON, M.D.

Chief of the Department of Genito-Urinary Diseases and Dermatology, Bronx
Hospital and Dispensary; Editor of "The Critic and Guide"; Author of:
Treatment of Sexual Impotence and Other Sexual Disorders in Men
and Women; Treatment of Gonorrhea; Woman, Her Sex and Love
Life; Married Life and Happiness; Sexual Problems of Today; Sex
Knowledge for Men and Boys; Birth Control or the Limitation
of Offspring; Never Told Tales; Stories of Love and Life;
A Clergyman's Son and Daughter; Eugenics and Marriage;
Sex Knowledge for Women and Girls; Sex-Morality—Past,
Present and Future; Sexual Truths; Prescription In-
compatibilities, etc.; Ex-President of the Berlin Anglo-
American Medical Society, Fellow of the New York
Academy of Medicine; Fellow of the American
Medical Association; Member of the New York
State Medical Society, Medical Society of the
County of New York, Harlem Medical Asso-
ciation, American Medical Editors' Associa-
tion, American Urological Association, In-
ternationale Gesellschaft für Sexual-
forschung, British Society for the
Study of Sex Psychology, American Association for the Advance-
ment of Science, etc., etc.
Editor Dr. A. Jacobi's Collected Works

With an Introduction by
A. JACOBI, M.D., LL.D.
Late President of the American Medical Association

FORTY-SIXTH EDITION

Revised and Enlarged

1929

EUGENICS PUBLISHING CO., Inc.

NEW YORK

Whoever hesitates to utter that which he thinks the highest truth, lest it should be too much in advance of the time, may reassure himself by looking at his acts from an impersonal point of view. Let him duly realize the fact that opinion is the agency thru which character adapts external arrangements to itself — that his opinion rightly forms part of this agency—is a unit of force, constituting, with other such units, the general power which works out social changes; and he will perceive that he may properly give full utterance to his innermost conviction: leaving it to produce what effect it may. It is not for nothing that he has in him these sympathies with some principles and repugnance to others. He, with all his capacities, and aspirations, and beliefs, is not an accident, but a product of the time. He must remember that while he is a descendant of the past, he is a parent of the future; and that his thoughts are as children born to him, which he may not carelessly let die. . . . Not as adventitious therefore will the wise man regard the faith which is in him. The highest truth he sees he will fearlessly utter; knowing that, let what may come of it, he is thus playing his right part in the world — knowing that if he can effect the change he aims at, well: if not — well also; tho not so well.—HERBERT SPENCER.

PREFACE

For over twenty years, namely since the very beginning of my medical practice, I have been convinced of the very great importance, I might say of the life-and-death importance, of the knowledge of preventing conception, of avoiding undesired pregnancy. A large portion of the work of the general practitioner consists of confinements, and it did not take me very long to observe that what is supposed to be a blessing, and is still hypocritically spoken of as such, was often considered a curse, or at least a very undesirable event. And this not only among the poor, but also among those who were fairly well off. During the ten years that I was in general practice the conviction, based upon experience, upon what I saw with my own eyes, grew stronger and stronger with each year. I saw that in many cases an unexpected pregnancy, an undesired child was considered the most terrible calamity that could befall the family. I saw, as a result of it, the deepest anguish, the most acute suffering; I saw physical, mental and economic ruin; and I saw death—death by infection and death by suicide.

And I determined to do all *I* could to change this state of affairs. I determined to devote my feeble pen and my leisure time to these things: First, to advocating the propriety of preventing conception, of limiting the number of one's children according to one's economic means and other circumstances; second, to a study of the best, safest and most harmless means of preventing conception; and third, to a dissemination of this knowledge among the medical profession, and thru it, among the laity. In the beginning my efforts could be but feeble and sporadic, and the results correspondingly slight. But during the past ten years, as leisure and financial ease increased, as my standing and influence in the profession grew stronger, I have been hammering at the subject incessantly. At every possible opportunity, by the aid of lectures, pamphlets, letters to editors, articles in medical journals and in newspapers and books, I have endeavored to bring the subject to the attention of the medical profession and of the laity. And I am glad to say, that the propaganda has been bearing fruit. The laity listened eagerly from the first; but it was a Sisyphus' work indeed to move the medical profession. What its mental state was on the subject (as well as on some other subjects) when I started the advocacy of my ideas, I would rather not say; the language might be slightly unparliamentary; and its attitude towards me was anything but brotherly: I was a crank, an extremist (this was the mildest judgment), my ideas were pernicious and criminal; I should be forced to shut up, and some even generously suggested that I ought to be deprived of my membership in the various national and local medical societies. But when I am convinced of the truth of a thing, then the opposition and threats of enemies, as well as the well-meant warnings of friends, act on me only as a stimulant to greater endeavors. And I have always been convinced that truth, presented persistently, convincingly and from different angles, cannot fail to make its impress, except on crania that are utterly impenetrable to reason, to proof, to argument. And my conviction has proved its correctness. Not only have I made tens of thousands of converts among people who had no fixed ideas on the subject or who were on the borderland, but thousands of those who sneered and stupidly shrugged their shoulders, are now acknowledging that I am doing work of the utmost humanitarian importance, and feel flattered by my recognition of them and honored by my friendship. So goes the world.

I thought it would be a good thing to incorporate in one book *all* the arguments in favor of the volitional control of the birth rate, *all* arguments in favor of spreading the knowledge of the prevention of conception among the people, and to answer *all* arguments and so-called arguments of those who object to the prevention of conception propaganda. This attempt is presented in this book. I intend it to present the last word on the subject, and to present the subject from every point of view. I expect this little volume to become the manual of all those who believe with the author that there is no other measure that would so positively, so immediately, contribute toward the happiness and progress of the human race as would teaching the people the proper means of prevention of conception.

NOTE. Some might doubt the timeliness of getting out such a book at the present moment, when millions of crazed people are crushing one another's lives out, and when the weakened and decimated nations will try to make up their diminished populations by an increased birth rate. On the contrary: considering, as we do, overpopulation as one of the causes of war, this book becomes doubly timely. And, then, fortunately we in this country are not engaged in the horrible carnage, and we are not running any risks of sudden decimation.

W. J. R.

April 3d, 1915.

PREFACE TO THE FIFTH EDITION

No change has taken place in our federal or State laws since this book made its appearance, eight months ago; the laws against contraceptive information are still on our statute books in all their stupid malignity. But a tremendous change has taken place in public opinion; the people who want the information *are* obtaining it, and the problem which is of such vital interest to the individual and to the race *is gradually solving itself,* without the aid and in spite of our legislators.

January 1st, 1916.

PREFACE TO THE ELEVENTH EDITION

Barely twenty-two months have elapsed since the first edition of this book made its appearance. This is the eleventh edition. We may take it as a fair indication that the book is filling a real want, that all those who wish to preach birth-control, as well as those who wish to know the arguments pro and con this burning question of the day, find the book indispensable. And indispensable it will remain for many years to come. For it is a great error to assume that the victory has already been won or is about to be won soon. We are marching towards victory, but we are still far from it. And each step forward that we make intensifies the antagonism and the vindictiveness of the medieval reactionaries, and the victims who are unfortunate to get into their clutches are dealt with very severely. Only very recently Dr. Ben Reitman, Emma Goldman's coworker, was sentenced in Cleveland, O., by a judge, of whom the less said the better, to six months in prison and a 1,000-dollar fine—the extreme penalty in the State of Ohio. If the extreme penalty for imparting contraceptive information were imprisonment for life, Dr. Reitman would undoubtedly have gotten imprisonment for life—so merciful was this broad-minded judge. And Mrs. Sanger is now serving thirty days in Long Island City Jail, while her sister, Mrs. Ethel Byrne, is recovering from the effect of an eleven days' hunger strike.

No, the victory has not been won yet, and there is still room for at least a million copies of this

PREFACE

little volume. That the book is making **converts,** is beyond any question. Many people have told us that they had been opposed to birth-control, and purchased the book just to see what its advocates had to say; but after reading the book once or twice, they found themselves converted. And some of them have become zealous and energetic propagandists.

Those who are *earnestly* interested in birth-control can render no better service to the cause than by helping to spread this volume. For as a propaganda book there is none like it, or similar to it, in the English language, or in any other language with which we are familiar. It handles the subject in such a manner that the reader, unless an intellectual infant or a theologic slave, cannot help admitting that our arguments are unanswerable.

Help to spread this volume broadcast.

W. J. R.

12 Mount Morris Park W.,
New York City.
Lincoln's Birthday, 1917.

PREFACE TO THE 23rd EDITION.

A cloud of black reaction is hanging like a pall over this country. In spite of it the Birth Control Movement is making steady progress. This is the only ray of light in the drab and dreary darkness.

We believe we are justified in stating that this little book has been the most potent single factor in the spread of ideas of the rational limitation of offspring in the United States of America. May this, the 23rd edition, prove as effective and beneficent in this work of enlightenment as have the previous twenty-two editions.

August 1st, 1922.

PREFACE

to the

TWENTY FIFTH EDITION

The author can look back with pardonable pride upon the quarter century of his activity in the Birth Control Movement in this country.

The criminal war, and the still more criminal peace, and particularly the insane militarism of France, have had the effect of putting every liberal movement backward, of halting the progress of every humanitarian cause, in every country in the world. The Birth Control Movement alone has not shared the fate of other causes and has gone steadily forward.

It is hard to apportion with exactness the influence which any man has exerted on a certain cause, but as far as books are concerned, it is safe to say that this little volume has done greater service, has accomplished more, than any other. Its very simplicity makes it invaluable for those who need it most—the people at large. And the author confesses that it is with a glow of satisfaction that he signs his name to this, the Twenty-Fifth edition of Birth Control or The Limitation of Offspring by Prevenception.

WILLIAM J. ROBINSON, M. D.
December 8, 1923.

INTRODUCTION

The author of this new book was good enough to remind me of a few passages contained in my Presidential address delivered before the American Medical Association at its meeting in Atlantic City, in 1912. I asked the question whether there was no way to prevent those who were born into this world from becoming incompetent both physically and mentally. That seemed almost impossible as long as the riches provided by nature and industry were accessible to a part of the nation only. That was why it became an irresistible suggestion that only a certain number of infants should be born. Indeed as long as even the well to do limit the number of their offspring, the advice given the poor, or those to whom the raising of a large family is a task of difficulty or impossibility, to limit the number of their children—even the healthy ones— is more than merely excusable.

The case is worse when unhealthy, sick, sickly or infected and contagious children are born. Such an occurrence is a misfortune to the newcomer, to his parents and to society. The least that must be demanded is a clean bill of health. That is why I have often praised clergymen for good citizenship who refuse to marry couples without such a clean bill of health; and the health departments should see to it that contagious sexual diseases should be reported, watched and cured. Nor is this all. Hereditary influences propagate epilepsy, idiocy, feeblemindedness and criminality. Persons thus affected must not be permitted to propagate their ailments. This should be manifestly self-evident. The contrary should be declared

detrimental to the welfare of the commonwealth and punishable.

But this book treats of the subject from
many more points of view. The congestion of the population has proved dangerous even when the nation consists of
normally average individuals, originally
healthy and competent. Hunger, neg-
lect, poverty and chronic ailment have
caused and will continue to cause the appearance of malthusians and neomalthu-
sians, and the question whether a family
may be large or ought to be small, will
always be asked again and again. There
is only one country in which that question
is regarded with hypocritical sneers, that
country is ours; there is only one country
in which a man and woman must not
think of framing their own future, and
constructing their fate and that of their
born or unborn children—that is the land
of the "free."

It is my opinion that the individual and

collective habits in this regard should not be guided by other than voluntary self-determination. Indeed as long as the state is founded on the family, the man and the woman must not and cannot be interfered with by anything but their own will. Parental responsibility alone must control the numerical strength of a family; the prevention of excessive offspring is a central problem of both individual and social hygiene. This problem is of such magnitude that it cannot be solved by partial or hurried study, by denying its existence or by sneers and ridicule. Medicine, political economy, and far-seeing statesmanship should combine to solve it and help accomplish the ends of mankind.

The reduction of the number of children in the family is becoming a universal experience in all civilized countries. There is no cultured country at present in which the fact has not been noticed and studied. Since Octavianus and Napoleon the increase in the number of the non-married and the decrease of human war-material have been observed with misgivings; and to-day's several war-lords pray for more millions of slayable men. But before this year of wholesale annihilation of the vigorous and young, white and yellow and black, the statisticians, sociologists and physicians have created a literature in newspapers, magazines and books of all languages dealing intelligently with the subject under discussion. Like sensible people, not like our own fanatics, they have not only established the facts of the decrease of births and of the general population, but have studied the methods of birth-regulation, which could be used in an orderly and harmless manner.

While I am anxious to leave the questions involved to the author of this book, whose profound study and moderation I have had many opportunities to admire, I urge the readers not to pass by other literature on the subject. Within the last few months Prof. A. Grotjahn has enriched it by his lucid and comprehensive work, *Geburten-Rückgang und Geburten-Regelung* (Berlin, 1914). Doctors and nurses and other intellectual people will learn from it, and from this new book of Dr. Robinson's, and from their own analytical thinking, that both our Federal and state laws on the subject of prevention are grievously wrong and unjust.

It is important that these laws be repealed at the earliest possible moment; it is important that useful teaching be not crippled, that personal freedom be not interfered with, that the independence of married couples be protected, that families be safeguarded in regard to health and comfort, and that the future children of the nation be prepared for competent and comfortable citizenship.

A. Jacobi.

CONTENTS

CONTENTS

CONTENTS

ARTICLES FROM THE CRITIC AND GUIDE

THE LIMITATION OF OFFSPRING

BY THE

PREVENTION OF CONCEPTION

CHAPTER I

WHAT WE—THE WRITER AND HIS FOL-
LOWERS—STAND FOR

The subject which we are about to discuss is one of transcendent importance.
I know of no single question that is of
such far-reaching, vital importance to the
human race. Directly or indirectly it
touches every man, woman and child—nay
more, it touches not only the living child,
it touches the child not yet born. If I
have devoted so much time to a discussion
of this subject by pen and by word of
mouth, it is because I sincerely believe
that upon the proper solution of this ques-

tion depends, to a great extent, the welfare of the human race, the welfare of those living and of those to come after us.

But before we can discuss any question intelligently we must know just what the subject under discussion is. It is easy to approve or to condemn, but before you have a right to either approve or condemn, before you can do so honestly and conscientiously, you must know what it is that we advocate, what it is that we preach and demand.

Briefly it is this. We believe that under any conditions and particularly under our present economic conditions, human beings should be able to control the number of their offspring. They should be able to decide, how many children they want to have and when they want to have them. And to accomplish this result we demand that the knowledge of controlling the number of offspring, in other and plainer words, the knowledge of preventing undesirable conception, should *not* be considered criminal knowledge, that its dissemination should *not* be considered a criminal offense punishable by hard labor in Federal prisons, but that it should be considered knowledge useful and necessary to the welfare of the race and of the individual; and that its dissemination should be as permissible and as respectable as is the dissemination of any hygienic, sanitary or eugenic knowledge.

There is no element of force in our teachings; that is, we would not force any family to limit the number of their children against their will, tho we would endeavor to create a public opinion which would consider it a disgrace for any family to have more children than they can bring up and educate properly. We would consider it a disgrace, an anti-social act for any family to bring children into the world whom they must send out at an early age into the mills, shops and streets to earn a living, or must fall back upon public charity to save them from starvation. Public opinion is stronger than any laws, and in time people would be as much ashamed of having children whom they could not bring up properly in every sense of the word, as they are now ashamed of having their children turn out criminals.

Now, no disgrace can attach to any poor family, no matter how many children they have, because they have not got the knowledge, because society *prevents* them from having the knowledge of how to limit the number of children. But if that knowledge became easily accessible and people still refused to avail themselves of it, then they would properly be considered as antisocial, as criminal members of the community.

As far as couples are concerned who are well-to-do, who love children, and who are well capable of taking care of a

large number, we, that is, we American
limitationists, would put no limit. On
the contrary, we would say: "God bless
you, have as many children as you want
to; there is plenty of room yet for all of
you."

And I might as well state here that in
this respect we differ from our neo-malthusian friends in European countries
with whom we are otherwise in perfect
accord. Our European neo-malthusian
friends would put a limit to the number of
children even of the well-to-do and rich.
They claim that the means of subsistence
are but limited, that Europe, that is Western Europe, is about as thickly popu-
lated as it can be. And they are afraid
that the birth of a large number of people,
even among rich and well-to-do, means the
taking out of the bread from the mouths
of somebody, from the mouths of the poor.
We are not afraid of it. We know that
America can support in perfect comfort

millions and millions more of people. This shows how geography and economic conditions influence our opinions.

Our neo-malthusian friends across the sea are actuated in their propaganda more by the fear of a famine that will eventually stare the race in the face if the proper check is not put upon the birth rate. Their propaganda is more racial, national.

I, on the other hand, was drawn into the limitation of offspring propaganda by the individual sufferings and misery resulting from too many children which I witnessed among my friends and acquaintances and, as stated in the preface, among my patients in the early years of my practice. Not that I do not recognize that, eventually, in the future, the race will, in self-preservation, have to put a strong check upon its birth rate, but I am dealing, I always prefer to deal, with the present, with the living people of to-day.

Somehow or other I have always been of the opinion that if we deal intelligently with the present we can safely let the future take care of itself. I even recognize that some countries of Europe are even now so overpopulated that a check has become necessary, but I am dealing with the United States and not with Europe; one country at a time is enough. Let our European friends deal with the problems which confront them. They can do so more intelligently, more efficiently, than we.

Chapter II

THE SPECTER OF TOO MANY CHILDREN

The effects of the limitation of off-spring might be discussed under two separate heads: the effects upon the individual family, and the effects upon the race as a whole. But this subdivision would really be an artificial one. You cannot injure or benefit the individual without injuring or benefiting the race, and you cannot injure or benefit the race without injuring or benefiting the individual. The race is not something abstract, separate, apart from the individuals composing it, any more than the body is something different and apart from the cells and organs composing it. The body is healthy just in proportion to the health and harmonious working of its individual cells. If in a nation of one million people one person is unhappy and inefficient, that nation is one-millionth unhappy and inefficient. If five hundred thousand individuals of that nation are unhappy and inefficient, then that race is one-half unhappy and inefficient. And if every individual in that race is unhappy and inefficient the entire race is unhappy and inefficient. It is, therefore, the individual and the individual family that we have to look out for, and if each individual is brought to the highest standard of happiness and efficiency we need not worry about the race; the entire race will be happy and efficient.*

* In this connection, that is the relative value of the mass and of the individual, I am inclined to agree with old Rosegger who says: "It is constantly taught that the hope of humanity is in the absorption of the individual in the mass. It seems to me that such hope lies in the preservation of personality. The nation, as a nation, is of no worth; such value as it has is because of the many personalities it embraces, and whose projects are to be protected by it. As to the doctrine of 'the individual for the state, and not the state for the indi-

That under our present economic conditions the fear of too many children is a most frightful specter which terrorizes the ordinary workman and the middle class and professional man, is something which requires no discussion. Anybody who has eyes to see, sees it on every side. There would not be this frenzied search and demand for contraceptive knowledge if this were not so. That an unlimited number of children is a curse to the poor, requires almost no argument. There is not a physician who has not had cases in his practice of families which started life in a respectable manner but which became quickly demoralized, financially and physically, by children coming in rapid succession. Every physician will tell you the gradual change in feelings on the part of

vidual,' it may, in times of great peril, happen that for a brief period it shall prevail, so that of a thousand individuals a strong body is created, as in war, or under tyrannic oppression. When this danger is past, the mass, of necessity, disintegrates."

the parents with the appearance of each successive child. While the first child and perhaps the second are generally received with genuine joy, unless they come too soon after marriage, the third and fourth are met with indifference, while the fifth and succeeding ones are considered catastrophes, and many a father and mother hope for a miscarriage or pray that it be still-born or be carried off soon after birth. And many a physician will tell you of cases in which their endeavors to bring to life a still-born child were not at all considered by the parents, by the father particularly, with favor. More than one physician told me that when practicing artificial respiration on a new-born babe he was told by the father to leave the child alone, that it was not worth while bothering about.

That a family of three or four can live better, more comfortably, on a certain sum per week, say twenty-five dollars, than can a family of six or seven, goes without saying.   Only the obtusest mind will deny that, and still it is being denied day after day.   But we will deal with this point later on.

A workingman should not have more than two children.   Every child after the second, and particularly after the third, is individually and racially a calamity.   It means that the mother's health is being exhausted, it means that she cannot attend as properly as she should to her first children, it means that the succeeding children are taking away a part of the indispensable food and clothing from the first children, it means that the first children will not be able to get the necessary bringing up and education that they otherwise would, it means that they will be sent to work earlier than they otherwise would, it means glutting the labor market with wage-slaves.   In short, in my opinion, too many children in other than well-to-do

families is a crime.   It is a crime against
every member of the individual family, a
crime against the father, a crime against
the mother, a crime against the first children, a crime against the succeeding children, and a crime against society.

Chapter III

THE ORTHODOX REMEDIES

This being so, what is the remedy?
Two remedies are proposed by our reactionary philosophers and sociologists.
One is that the poor should not marry
until they are able to support a family, or
they should marry late in life. This advice is as stupid as it is vicious. If the
poor, embracing in this term not only the
workingmen but many professional men,
writers, small business men, etc., were to
wait until they could support a family
properly, they would not be able to marry
while alive. They would have to wait until they went to heaven, or until they were
in their second incarnation. But if the
advice to marry late were universally followed, it would prove an irreparable in-

jury to the human race. It would mean an indescribable increase in prostitution, in sexual perversions, in sexual weakness, and in venereal disease. The fathers would come to their nuptial beds sapped of all vitality, debilitated, infected. And as late marriages among men mean necessarily also late marriages among women, the mothers would be neurotic or psychotic old maids, and what children such unions would give rise to can readily be imagined.

The second advice is to abstain—that married people should abstain from sexual relations. To give advice which we know is impossible of being followed is the acme of fatuity. But where married people were foolish enough to attempt to follow this advice the effects were pernicious. For married people to attempt to abstain for any length of time means to lay the foundation for irritability, weakness, nervousness, or even genuine neuroses, and a cooling or even destruction of the affections. It means more, it very often means driving the husband into the arms of prostitutes, with the possible risks of venereal disease.

Considered from every point of view these two pieces of advice, to marry late or to abstain when married, are useless, because impracticable and pernicious, because if they could be followed they would result in pitiful injury to the individuals concerned and consequently to the race.

But a remedy must be had. We have found remedies for most ills that afflict the human organism, and it is only a matter of time when we will find remedies even for those ills that are still baffling us. The chief thing that distinguishes the human being from other animals is his intellect. It is by the aid of the intellect alone that we have been fighting and conquering Nature, wresting from her and unraveling her secrets, balking her at every step when it becomes necessary for our welfare. The human intellect has given us remedies which, while permitting men and women to marry at the proper age and to live a normal sexual life as Nature intended, still help them to control the number of their children. And try as I may, I cannot see what there is wrong in people who cannot afford to have many children using means which will prevent them from having many, which will help them to have just as many as they wish to have and can afford to have, and just at such times as they wish to have them.

Before we proceed further, it will be best to consider the objections which the opponents of the rational limitation of offspring have to offer. The objections are many in number, but the unbiased reader will admit that none of them have a solid foundation, that none of them are unanswerable.

CHAPTER IV

THE RACE SUICIDE BUGBEAR

The first objection we are apt to hear, when we advocate that the knowledge of the use of preventives be easily accessible, is that such knowledge would have dire effects, that it would decrease the population to such a degree that it would soon come to a standstill, then it would begin gradually to diminish and finally to die out—in other words, that the human race would commit suicide. That this objection is worthless we can prove by a consideration of individual families as well as by a consideration of entire nations. Are families who possess a knowledge of efficient and harmless preventives perfectly childless? Of course not. There are *hundreds of thousands* of families now thruout the world who employ artificial preventives regularly, but very few of them are altogether childless. They have one, two or three or even four children. They regulate the time when they want to have the children and their number, but very few indeed decide to remain barren altogether.

That there is a small percentage of men and women who are so devoid of the parental impulse that they would utilize the preventives so as never to have any children I will admit. But I ask you in all seriousness: Is it not better for the race that people who are so utterly devoid of that something that we call the parental instinct that they do not want to have any children at all, should not have any? Is a child conceived, born and brought up against the will of the parents a spectacle to be enthusiastic over? On the contrary. In my opinion this fact is rather in favor of the use of artificial preventives, in that

the race can speedily eliminate those men
and women who under no circumstances
wish to become fathers and mothers.

When I see to what interminable trouble and expense some men and women
go in order to have children; when I see
what tortures and risks, endangering her
very life—I am speaking of numerous
Cesarean sections—a prospective mother
will undergo in order to have a living
child, I have no fear that the use of preventives will result in the dying out of
the human race.

What I say is not based upon hearsay,
upon theory, but upon actual knowledge,
mostly upon personal experience with
friends and patients.   Just as I have seen
the bride and bridegroom beg for a contraceptive because they wanted to get
married and could not just yet afford to
have children, just as I have seen the
mothers with five or six children weeping
bitter tears and almost going down on

their knees praying to give them something to avoid the horror of another child, just so have I had the wife and husband married for some time but still childless, begging me with anguish and anxiety to do something for them so that they could have one or several children.   As a matter of fact, treatment for sterility of either the husband or wife or both constitutes a very substantial part of the author's practice.   And I know of no greater joy than that of the married woman who had been childless for several years and has finally become a mother.

It is, one must admit, the height of folly to argue that because people object to six or a dozen children, they would object to two or three.   No, there is no danger of the parental instinct dying out.   I even deny that this instinct is now weaker or more attenuated than it was fifty or a hundred years ago.   True, our ancestors had a larger progeny than we have, but the reasons for this can be found elsewhere than in a strong parental instinct. Those reasons, for a large progeny, may be stated as follows: First, they could not help themselves. At that time means for the prevention of conception were practically unknown, and no matter how anxious a father or a mother (particularly the latter) might have been to put a check to further procreation, they knew of no method except abstinence, a method which was never very popular. And this brings us to the second reason. Our ancestors were generally more intemperate in rebus sexualibus, the same as in food and drink, than we are. This is true, all opinions to the contrary notwithstanding. Their life was coarse, dull, monotonous, and this was their only pleasure, as it still is of those who belong to the lowest strata of society. And third, our ancestors lacked the sense of responsibility that we possess. They might have loved their children as much as we do, but our love is a finer love, more intelligent, more sublime, more anxious for the future.   In other words, the love of our ancestors for their children was more a selfish love, as is the love of the low and ignorant of the present day. Our love is a noble, altruistic one, which forces us occasionally to deprive ourselves of the pleasure of children for the children's own sake.   Again I say, there is no danger of the parental instinct dying out.

But we have better proofs—proofs unanswerable and undeniable.   Here we have a whole country, Holland, in which the prevention of conception is legally sanctioned, in which the use of preventives is practically universal—and is the country dying out?   On the contrary, it is increasing even somewhat more rapidly than before, because we have this remarkable and gratifying phenomenon to bear in mind, that wherever the birth rate goes down the death rate goes down *pari passu,* or even to a still greater degree. This can be proven by statistics from almost every country in the world. For instance, in 1910 the birth rate in Holland was 32 and the mortality 18, in 1912 the birth rate fell to 28 but then the mortality rate fell still lower, namely to 12, so we see that there is an actual gain even in population, instead of a loss. And the physical constitution of the people has been improving. The proportion of recruits for instance over 5 ft. 7 in. in height was increased from 24 to 47 per cent., while that of those under 5 ft. 2½ in. has fallen from 25 to 8 per cent. (Drysdale). And in New Zealand, where the sale of contraceptives is practically free, the birth rate is now 20 and the mortality rate is 10. Does that look like race suicide? On the contrary, there is a steady increase at the rate of ten per cent., while sickness and death of children, with their attendant

economic and emotional waste, are reduced to a minimum.

DECREASED BIRTH-RATE MEANS DECREASED INFANTILE DEATH RATE

This decrease of the death rate is very
easy to understand, because the fewer children a mother has the better care she can
take of those she does have. The economic condition of families with fewer
children is better than of families with
many children, speaking, of course, of the
same strata of society.   And the mother's
health not being exhausted by too frequent child-bearing, nursing and bringing
up of children, her health is better and she
gives birth to healthier and more resistant
children.

An interesting study on this point was
made by Dr. Alice Hamilton (*Bulletin of
the American Academy of Medicine* for
May, 1910).   Sixteen hundred families
of wage earners were investigated, and the

results are contained in the following
table:

Deaths per 1000 Births in
 Families of 4 children and less, 118
 Families of 6 children,   267
 Families of 7 children,   280
 Families of 8 children,   291
 Families of 9 children and more, 303

Dr. Hamilton sums up her results as
follows: Our study of 1600 families of
the poorer working class shows that child
mortality increases proportionately as the
number of children per family increases,
until we have a death-rate in families of
8 children and over, which is *two and a
half* times as great as that in families of
4 children and under.

In short, in families that have few children a much larger proportion remain
alive, so that the balance is kept up fairly
well.

I admit that when the knowledge of the

use of preventives becomes really universal the rate of increase of the human
race will become very much slower. But
there is certainly a great difference between a slow increase and suicide. Why
is it necessary that the human race should
increase in numbers rapidly? I permit
myself here to quote a paragraph from another paper of mine on the same subject:

Is an increase in numbers so very desirable? In fact is it at all desirable? Ask
yourself that question, if it never occurred
to you before. Is there any greatness or
any happiness in numbers alone? Is China
with its more than four hundred millions
any happier than we, who can boast of
only ninety millions? And does China
from any and every point of view amount
to as much as does the United States,
which has only about one-fifth of its population? And would not any one of you
prefer to be a citizen of Italy, or Norway,
or Sweden, or the little republic of Swit-

zerland, which has fewer inhabitants than has New York City, than to be a subject of the brutal, murderous Russian Czar who reigns over one hundred and forty millions? No, there is no honor, and there should be no pride, in numbers merely.

I prefer a commonwealth of five million people, all of them healthy and contented, all doing congenial work, all having work to do, all materially comfortable, all educated and cultured, all free to think and free to express their thoughts, with high ideas of a greater future and a higher humanity, to an empire or a republic of a hundred millions, all fighting, all struggling, all cutting each other's throats, all in fear of starvation, with senseless luxury on one hand and shameful poverty on the other, with killing idleness on one hand and killing overwork on the other, with bursting over-satiation on the one hand and exhausting starvation on the other; with millions tramping the streets and highways naked and hungry, with millions of human beings illiterate, held in the clutches of superstition, selfishness and brutishness; with thousands and thousands of imbeciles, criminals, perverts, grafters, prostitutes— female prostitutes who sell their bodies and male prostitutes who sell their minds, their ideas and convictions—I prefer, I say, the above-described small to the above-described larger commonwealth.

No, numbers alone, I repeat, do not count. With Spencer, I despise that vulgar conception which considers a large population, large territory, and big commerce as its highest ideal, its noblest aim. With Spencer, I would say that, instead of an immense amount of life of low type, I would far sooner see half the amount of life of a high type.

THE CAUSE FOR ALARM LIES ELSEWHERE

There is one point, however, that should give all true friends of humanity cause for alarm. While the birth rate has decreased markedly in every civilized country in the world, in those countries in which the discussion of the use of preventives is prohibited, and in which the obtaining of preventive means is most difficult, the decrease in the birth rate has been most marked in the higher and in the well-to-do middle and professional classes.   In other words, in countries like England and the United States, the most marked diminution of the birth rate has been among the aristocracy, among the cultured classes, among artists, lawyers, physicians, clergymen, merchants, etc., while it has been but slightly diminished among the workmen and among the poor and very poor.   In fact, you can take it as an axiom that the number of children is in inverse ratio to the social standing, culture and earning capacity of the parents. In still other words, it means that those best fit to breed children, those most likely to transmit a desirable heredity, and those most able to bring up children, are breeding less and less, while those least able to and least capable of bringing up children and giving them a decent education and a decent start in life, and those most tainted with disease, with alcoholism, mental instability, epilepsy, insanity, moronism, etc., keep on breeding unrestrainedly. What that means for the future of a nation the most sluggish thinker can easily perceive. It means that, if no check be put to this state of affairs, eventually the mental and physical standard of the race will be lowered, that the race will begin to degenerate.

This is something which no true friend of humanity can contemplate with equanimity. But what is the remedy? To exhort, beg or command the better classes to become more prolific is, as you all know, practically useless. Nobody whose economic means or inclinations are against having many children will sacrifice himself or herself and have six or eight children instead of two or three, just in order to save the race. Nobody who has acquired the knowledge of limiting his offspring will throw that knowledge away, for altruism has not reached and will hardly ever reach this stage, and besides every man and woman will think: Oh, our two or three children will not make any difference. In other words, the better classes, or if you prefer the *so-called* better classes, will continue to have a very limited number of children—so the only remedy we have at command is to instruct the lower classes to make use of the same means so that they may not by their unrestricted breeding overwhelm the better elements, pollute the race-stock and add to human misery.

And this is what I would demand. I would demand that it be not only the right but the duty of the Departments of Health, of private practitioners and visiting district nurses to instruct the poor in simple and cheap methods of preventing undesirable pregnancies. This idea may be shocking to you by its novelty. But it is not so very novel at all. I have been advocating it for many years. And the time will come, is bound to come, when it will be seen to be the simplest kind of common sense and will be acted upon by all intelligent communities.

FRANCE

I cannot leave the subject of race suicide or depopulation without devoting a special paragraph to France. You know that France has always been the

bête noire of the anti-limitationists. It is
always held up to us as a horrible specter.
"See what your propaganda is apt to lead
to. Look at France. Depraved, morally and physically degenerate, decadent,
dying. A few decades more and there
will be no France. She will be swallowed
up by her stronger neighbors." Plausible as this indictment may be on a super-
ficial examination, it has one fault: it is
not true. But to show that it is not true,
I can do no better than to present the
answer to this indictment as given by Dr.
C. V. Drysdale of London, who is doing
such valiant work in putting the subject
of the rational limitation of offspring on
a solid, scientific, irrefutable basis. He
has collected the vital statistics for France
over the whole period of her declining
birth rate, i.e., from before the Revolution. (The Empire and the Birth-Rate.
By C. V. Drysdale, D.Sc. A paper
read before The Royal Colonial Institute,

March 24, 1914.) And what do these statistics show? They show:

"1. France is *not* becoming depopulated. Her population has been slowly but steadily rising ever since the Franco-German war, both actually and by excess of births over deaths, although in some years the deaths have exceeded the births.

"2. The excess of births over deaths in the last decade, 1901-10, though small, is double that of the previous decade, notwithstanding that the birth-rate fell from 22.2 to 20.6. It averaged about 48,000 per annum.

"3. In 1781-84, before the decline of the birth-rate set in, the birth-rate had the high value of 38.9 per thousand. But instead of this giving a high natural increase of population, the death-rate was no less than 37 per thousand, giving an excess of births over deaths of only 1.9 per thousand—little more than that (1.2) of the last decade.

"4. The enormous fall of the birth-rate from 38.9 to 20.6 per thousand, has been accompanied by a fall in the death-rate from 37 to 19.4 per thousand. Thus a fall of 18.3 in the birth-rate has been accompanied by a fall of 17.6 in the death-rate, and only a drop of .7 per thousand in the rate of increase.

"5. The present low rate of natural increase in France is not necessarily due to its low birth-rate, as Ontario in Canada, with a similar birth-rate, had a death-rate of 10 per thousand, or a natural increase of 9 per thousand—nearly as great as our own. The low increase of France is therefore due to its high death-rate, not to its low birth-rate, and an explanation or remedy should be found for the former before objection is made to the latter.

"6. Possibly as a result of the present agitation in France in favor of larger families, the births in the first half of last year increased by 8,000 over those of the corresponding period of 1912. *Instead of producing a greater increase of population, the deaths increased by 12,000, so that the survivals actually diminished."*

These facts, besides showing that France is not dying out, show also incidentally, what we have referred to many times before, that an increase in the birth rate does not even necessarily mean an increase in the population; because it can be, and often is, balanced or overbalanced by an increased death rate.

That there is less poverty, less wretchedness in France than in countries where the poor have not yet learned the secret of limiting their offspring, everybody will testify who has lived in France and in Italy or Spain, for instance. The difference is not so noticeable in the slums of large cities—they are wretched everywhere—but it is unmistakable in the smaller cities and in the villages.

As to the decadence of France, its

moral and physical degeneracy, I believe
that her dignified manly behavior during
this war, her efficient stubborn resistance,
her unity and readiness for the most extreme self-sacrifice will silence her worst
detractors and it seems likely that when
the war is over, no matter what its issue
may be, this accusation against France
will be relegated to the limbo of obsolete
and forgotten slanders.

One thing however I am willing to
admit and even to insist upon. It will
not do for one country to preach and practice extreme limitation of offspring, when
other countries breed unrestrainedly.
Just as it would be foolish to demand disarmament of one country, when that country's neighbors refuse to disarm. But
what is the remedy? The remedy is not
to give up preaching limitation of offspring, but preaching it in *all* countries.
Fortunately, the rational control of offspring is something that appeals to all

people, all classes, all nations (except those of the lowest moral and intellectual standing), and it is only necessary to introduce it into a country to find for it a ready and welcome acceptance, and this is the duty of all true, broad-minded humanitarians. I would say patriots, only this word has acquired a sinister meaning, often being used by chauvinists and jingoists as a cloak for their narrow and selfish designs.

Just as disarmament must be preached to all the world, so the limitation of offspring idea must be introduced to all nations at one and the same time.

CHAPTER V

IT WILL LEAD TO IMMORALITY

This objection seems to be the strongest one in the opinion of some even otherwise very rational thinkers. I have heard it from freethinkers, from socialists, and from some very sincere, cultured and educated men. People who have gotten over the "race suicide" bugaboo still consider this a serious objection to the popular spread of the knowledge of contraceptives. They are deeply afraid that if this knowledge became universal, immorality, by which they mean female unchastity, would become universal. They are convinced that what keeps our girls and other husbandless women chaste is the fear of pregnancy and nothing else. In other words, they openly acknowledge that our entire adult womanhood is mentally unchaste and what keeps a large proportion of them from physical unchastity is not morality but the fear of consequences.

To this argument, which next to the race suicide argument, seems to be the most formidable, and to a good many the most unanswerable, leaving out the answer that virtue which is such by fear is no virtue at all, and that virtue that needs continuous guarding is scarcely worth the sentinel, my answer is that the fear of pregnancy is not the chief deterrent. What keeps most of our unmarried women chaste is the general bringing up, the general and religious education, the custom of the country, hereditary influence, and the general monogamous tendency of the female.

On a certain percentage of the female population all these factors exert no influence now, and the only result the knowledge we advocate would have is that illicit relations would be entered upon with less terror, perhaps, with less anxiety than they are now, but *far from increasing immorality it would diminish it.* I will explain what I mean. The fear of pregnancy does act as a deterrent in a large number of cases to the performance of coitus in the natural, normal way, but instead of that it leads to numerous perversions of the sexual act, which are as a rule extremely injurious to the health of both partners. I know whereof I am speaking. I see daily the results of these sexual perversions in married couples, in engaged people and men and women who just keep company, and in men and women who are just acquainted; and I can assure you that while the fear of pregnancy, as I said, does act as a deterrent in many cases, say even in a large number of cases, it does not act as a check against sexual immorality. On the contrary, it

increases it, because I consider sexual perversions entered into out of fear of pregnancy more immoral than natural relations.

And I tell you there are thousands of
women who are physically virgins, whose
hymen is intact, but who are so expert in
various sexual perversions that they could
learn nothing new from Krafft-Ebing's
Psychopathia Sexualis, and such women,
such demi-vierges, are in my opinion much
more unchaste than the woman who enters
upon normal. tho illicit sexual relations,
with the man she loves.

And if some women are bound to have
illicit relations, is it not better that they
should know the use of a harmless preventive than that they should become
pregnant, disgracing and ostracizing
themselves, and their families, or that they
should subject themselves to the degradation and risks of an abortion, or failing
this take carbolic acid or bichloride, jump

into the river or throw themselves under the wheels of a running train? I may be wrong, my views may be strabismic, but I cannot help believing that I am kinder and humaner than those cruel bigots who demand that any woman who has indulged in illicit relations should expiate her "crime" by death or by all the humiliation, ostracism and suffering which are now imposed upon the mother of an illegitimate child.

No, I am quite sure that the knowledge of the use of preventives will not increase immorality, using that term as a synonym of female unchastity. It will merely change perversions and injurious practices into natural relations, which every humane and sane thinker must consider a gain and not a loss.

Chapter VI

IT IS INJURIOUS

This objection we still meet quite frequently, and we hear it not only from the laity, who are not supposed to know any better, but from physicians who are supposed to know better. A whole catalogue of ills are given which are likely to result from the use of preventives of conception: congestion, inflammation, cancer, nervousness, etc. This statement is unqualifiedly false. Physicians who make such statements do it either because they are ignorant or because they know only of some methods that *are* injurious, or confuse prevention of conception with abortion, or they do so deliberately to mislead the people, to prevent them from engaging in what they call an immoral, ungodly and demoralizing practice.

In a book entitled "Racial Decay,"

written with a zeal and earnestness worthy of a better cause, the author devotes pages and pages to the alleged pathologic consequences of prevention. But thruout the book he shows not only complete ignorance of the subject, which might be pardonable in a layman, but he shows a muddleheadedness which is inexcusable in anybody who ventures to discuss the important subject of the limitation of offspring. For all thru the book he speaks of prevention and abortion as if they were one and the same thing, and he dilates upon the injurious effects of coitus interruptus, a method which we ourselves, as well as every student of sexual pathology, condemn most emphatically, most unequivocally! Some vague cases taken from antiquated medical books are of absolutely no value, because the modern methods of prevention were unknown at that time, and because there is the same stupid confusion of prevention of conception with abortion, and the reports of injuries to the nervous condition of the woman all refer to coitus interruptus or conjugal onanism.

I emphasize: There is absolutely nothing injurious in the proper modern methods of prevention. On the contrary, more than once has it been noticed that women who suffered with congestion, leucorrhea, catarrh of the cervix and vagina, were improved by the use of modern contraceptives. Of course there is no doubt that there are injurious methods of prevention, that certain mechanical devices and poisonous solutions are in use which may in time produce injury to the parts. But are you going to condemn harmless methods because there are methods which are not harmless? Because decomposed food is injurious are you going to condemn all food? Because an alkaline soap is irritating are you going to condemn the use of all soap? It is absurd, and still this is the kind of argument the opponents of the limitation of offspring have recourse to. And I challenge any physician, any gynecologist to bring forth *a single* authenticated case in which disease or injury resulted from the use of the modern methods of prevention. I know they cannot do it.

CHAPTER VII

IT PRODUCES STERILITY

This is another one of the fallacies which are heard frequently from clerical and medical opponents of the limitation of offspring. It could have only originated from the confusion of prevention of conception with abortion, or again perhaps from the fact that those opponents have only known of methods which were particularly brutal and atrocious.

We know that the proper methods of

prevention have absolutely no effect whatever in causing sterility. As long as the woman uses the preventive she is safe, as soon as she gives up the use of the preventive she becomes impregnated. Sometimes a single omission of the use of the preventive measure causes impregnation, as many women have found out to their sorrow.

But the sterility bugaboo is firmly rooted. A couple came to me who wanted to have children. The woman wanted treatment. They had used preventives for three years and then, their circumstances having improved, they decided to have a child, but altho they had discontinued the use of preventives for over a year, no offspring had resulted. They were firmly convinced that the wife was sterile owing to the use of the contraceptives. As a matter of fact, repeated examinations showed that the husband was suffering from complete azoöspermia and

never could have any children, with or
without contraceptives.   But it was
plainly to be seen that these patients were
skeptical and clung to their belief that the
lack of offspring was due to the means of
preventing them which they had used in
the past.

Chapter VIII

IT IS NOT ABSOLUTELY SURE

Our opponents claim that there is no
absolutely sure means of the prevention
of conception, that the best of them fail
once in a while.   This is true and isn't
true.   It is true in the sense that there is
not one single method that is suitable for
everybody, but it is not true that a certain
means will not prove absolutely efficient
in a certain given case, or practically so.

And this uncertainty is due to the fact
that the whole thing is done secretly,

clandestinely, as if a crime were being committed. If the whole thing were free and legal, if the matter could be discussed freely in the journals, the best methods would be learned quickly enough, and each one would have no difficulty in finding the means most appropriate to herself.

But even as it is now, the methods are infallible in 98 or 99 per cent. of cases, and while this may be no consolation to the hundredth case that happens to be caught, we do consider that both for the individual family and for the race as a whole it is even now a means of the most wonderful potency for good.

One little instance: In Berlin the birth rate was, in 1876, 240 per annum per each thousand married women; in 1912 the birth rate had fallen to 90! Doesn't this show the great efficacy of contraceptive measures?

CHAPTER IX

WOULD LEAD TO EXCESS IN MARRIED LIFE

A minor objection that is hardly worth considering, but which I will take up nevertheless, because I heard it often in the discussions following my lectures is that, with such knowledge, married people will indulge to excess, thus ruining their constitutions. Here is again the same idea: that we abstain from moral crimes and physical sins only thru fear of the consequences.

I stamp this mediæval idea as false. Some people will commit sins, crimes and bestialities in spite of consequences; others will lead a healthy, moral, rational life just for its own sake, because they can't help being decent, because they have been brought up to be decent. And I am sure that when the study of sexual hygiene has become universal, when men know that excessive indulgence is injurious, they will abstain from it, the same as they abstain from excessive alcoholic indulgence or excessive eating. It is true, as Shaw says, that married life offers the maximum of temptation with the maximum of opportunity, but as the variety is lacking, things equalize themselves and the vast majority of married couples settle down after the first few months to a temperate existence, sexually speaking.

And then we must not forget that there is no short royal road to prevention. Every efficient method demands a little care, a little trouble, a little expense. And this alone will act as a check.

The times when husbands indulge most unrestrainedly because the fear of impregnation is absent, is during their wives' pregnancies; and as pregnancies will be fewer and farther between, there will be less indulgence. So that we have a right to claim, that far from increasing

indulgence in marital relations, a knowledge of the means of prevention will act
as a check, and excesses will give place to
moderation.

Chapter X

IT IS AGAINST RELIGION

I am not dealing here with pious hypo-
crites, but some very earnest and sincere
people have brought up this objection,
that the prevention of conception is reprehensible because it is against religion. I
know of no place in the Bible where the
prevention of conception or limitation of
offspring is prohibited. I do not claim to
be a great student of the Bible, but when
I spoke recently at St. Mark's Church this
point was brought up and the minister
said distinctly that he did not know, at
least he could not think at the time of
any place in either the Old or the New

Testament which contained anything condemning the use of preventives.

But assuming that it did contain an explicit injunction against their use, I would simply ask those whose conduct is guided by the Bible to refrain from using those means, but not to attempt to force their morals and their conduct upon people who are guided by different standards of morality.

And, besides, when a man brings in religion as an argument then no further discussion is possible. I do not sneer at religion, I can even sincerely respect a sincerely religious person, for I know that many of them are both earnest in their convictions and humanitarian in their endeavors, but I simply say that this is a question which we cannot discuss. Religion is a matter of faith and not reason; you believe so and so and that is all there is to it. Another man believes differently. Let him get his salvation in his

own way as long as he does not injure
you.

CHAPTER XI

IT IS IMMORAL

This argument is in the same class as
the religious argument. It all depends
on what you call immoral. Why the use
of a harmless mechanical or chemical
agent before or after coitus is more immoral than the use of the same or similar
thing by a woman suffering with leucorrhea, I cannot for the life of me see. No
inanimate thing, no act can be moral or
immoral per se. It is the circumstances
under which an act is performed, the uses
to which a thing is put that make it moral
or immoral. Immoral is something that
is injurious to the community, to another
individual, or to the person himself. As
I am showing in this book by the use of
irrefutable arguments and figures, the use

of such contraceptives is not injurious to the persons who are using them, they are certainly not injurious to one's neighbors, and far from being injurious to the community they are helpful to it by raising the hygienic, eugenic and economic standards. So wherein does the immorality consist?

I am afraid that those who bring up the immorality argument have created a fetish which they would find great difficulty in maintaining on its pedestal if forced to present real arguments. But, again, as I said in discussing the religious argument, some people have peculiar ideas as to what is moral and immoral, and if one has made up his mind that a certain action is immoral it is no use discussing matters. Such people are generally impervious to argument. As to those men who go even further and say that wives who use preventives are nothing but monogamous prostitutes, and I have heard that

argument from apparently sane people,
one of them even calling himself a socialist, I can only say that with such people it
is useless to argue. We can only give
them tit for tat by calling them imbeciles.

CHAPTER XII

IT LEADS TO DIVORCE

We are told that childlessness is one of
the causes of divorce, and statistics seem
to show that there is more divorce among
childless couples than among those who
have children. Let us examine this question in detail.

First comes the general question: Is
divorce in itself an unmitigated evil? Is
it better that people who no longer care to
live with each other, or who have found it
impossible to live with each other, who perhaps hate and loathe each other, should be
forced to live together by extraneous cir-

cumstances and obstacles, or is it better
that such people should be free to go their
way and perhaps find new, more congenial
partners?   Upon the answer to this question will depend the attitude of the person
who believes that childlessness is one of
the causes of divorce, for we must admit
that in many cases the presence of children, the fact that they have to be brought
up and cared for itself acts as a restraint,
as a barrier to divorce.

But those who bring this argument forget one very important point.   Most cases
of divorce in which childlessness is the
causative factor are due not to the fact
that the parents used preventive measures,
but to the fact that one of the partners,
either the husband or the wife, *was sterile*.
In other words, the divorce is not caused
by the desire of the parents *not* to have
any children, but by the desire *to have*
them, a desire which is frustrated by the
inability of either one or both partners.

In all cases of divorce of which I know in which the partners were childless, the divorce was demanded by one of the partners just because he or she was extremely anxious to have children, and they hoped that by remarrying their ardent desire would be realized. No, prevention of conception plays but an insignificant part in the increase of divorce.

To summarize: divorce in itself cannot be considered an unmitigated evil—in many cases it is an unmitigated blessing, freeing two people from a yoke that has become hateful to one or both; and *voluntary* childlessness plays a very small rôle in the divorce problem; it is involuntary childlessness or sterility that does play an important part, and for this the prevention of conception propaganda is certainly not responsible.

Chapter XIII

THE ONE CHILD ARGUMENT

We are told that it is bad to have one child only, for the child's own sake; that an only child is generally petted and coddled too much, too much anxiety is shown for his slightest ailment, and the result is that an only child usually grows up sickly, egotistic, disagreeable, handicapped in many ways, and incapable of taking his proper part in the world's battle. And here are our answers to this criticism.

First, I fully believe that rational parents, who know something about education and about the physiology and psychology of a child, can bring up even an only child into a normal human being. We have sickly and egotistical children in large families, and on the other hand we have finely brought up children where there are only two or three of them. It is not so much a matter of the number of children as of the quality of the parents.

And second, we have never advocated the one child system. We have always stated that in our opinion the proper number is two or three. But we must give the parents the right to decide upon the number and upon the time of the appearance of the children.

Chapter XIV

PREVENTING BIRTH OF GENIUSES

Another objection is that by preventing conception we may prevent the birth of some very great genius, of some wonderful thinker, philosopher, writer or artist. Yes, we may—everything is possible. But just as we may prevent the birth of a great man, that very same prevention may prevent the birth of some monster, of some wretched murderer, of some malicious criminal, of some anti-social beast.

And again, if this is to be taken as an argument, then every act of abstinence is a crime, for how can we know that but for the abstinence at a certain given time some wonderful man might not have been born nine months later?

No, among the millions that are born geniuses and saviors are very few and far between, and we certainly have a right to believe that by preventing conception we prevent many more undesirable than desirable human beings.

Chapter XV

CHILDREN SUPPORT PARENTS IN THEIR OLD AGE

Another argument is that children often prove a blessing and support to the parents when the latter get old. I do not deny that. But must we have half a dozen for that purpose? Are not two or three sufficient? And while it is true that some children do prove a blessing and support to their parents, many others prove a curse and a burden as long as they live. And there are certainly many more parents who wear themselves out and become prematurely aged in the struggle for existence, a struggle which is the more intense the more children there are at home, than are afterwards supported by their children.

And besides it is a pretty, pretty sad state of affairs that parents who have worked all their lives should in their old age be so poor as to need the support of their children. A society that permits that is rotten, and such conditions will not be permitted to last long.

I do not deny the force of this argument. I myself know people who were intensely poor, who struggled fearfully to bring up and educate their children, and now the latter have attained lucrative positions and have made the lot of their parents very much easier. But these are exceptional cases. And, besides, the argument is a very selfish one. To bring children into the world, to have them suffer the first twenty or twenty-five years of their lives, merely in order afterwards to be supported by them! Does that argument appeal to you? It does not appeal to me.

Chapter XVI

WOULD SMALL FAMILIES TEND TO DIMINISH WAGES?

Whether or not the universal knowledge of the limitation of offspring would tend to bring about the coöperative commonwealth is a question open to discussion. Some may believe it would, others not. I personally believe it would. By diminishing the number of the unemployed, by improving the material condition of the working people and thus giving them more time for study, for leisure and reading, etc., it would be greatly helpful in creating an intelligent class-conscious working class. But as I stated before this is a question open to discussion, but it is not open to discussion that a man getting fifteen dollars or twenty dollars or twenty-five dollars a week can live much more comfortably, much more healthfully, much more happily with two children than with six, and it requires a peculiarly obtuse mind to attempt to controvert this proposition.

And whether or not the conscious limitation of offspring will prove an effective revolutionary weapon and will serve to bring about the millennium, worries me very little. As I have said many times before, I am not dealing with future contingencies and with future generations. I am dealing with the present and with the people of to-day. If we will take care of the present the future will take care of itself. And when a poor woman, exhausted with several labors and with the bringing up of six or eight children, comes in to me or to you and with bitter tears begs to be saved from another pregnancy, it is the acme of cruelty and bigoted idiocy to tell her that the prevention of conception is not a panacea against wage slavery, that it will not improve the condition of the working class as a whole, that capitalism will find some means of keeping her and her children in subjection and in misery all the same, that by the operation of the "iron law of wages" her husband's wages will be diminished as soon as the capitalists find that they require less to live on, etc.

Every thinking man of the present day knows that the so-called "iron law of wages" is a myth, that the minimum necessary to support life is not the factor that determines the size of the wages. Wages are determined by a number of other factors, such as the supply and demand in the labor market, the standard of living in a given period in a given country, and very important, the efficiency and class-consciousness of the labor organizations. And if the law of supply and demand holds good in the labor market as it holds

good elsewhere, then it stands to reason
that the fewer wage-slaves we have, the
less glutted the labor market is, the higher
the wages are apt to be.

It may seem incredible but it is a fact
the truth of which can be incontrovertibly
proven that there are still Socialists who
fear a gradual improvement in the material conditions of the working people.
They fear that if their condition becomes
more comfortable they will lose the revolutionary spirit and sink into the mire of
self-content.   They verily believe that the
worse the condition of the workingman
the better it is for the "revolution."   This
attitude was very well demonstrated at the
meetings held under the auspices of the
Socialist Party in Berlin on August 22
and August 29, 1913. Some of the
speakers violently objected to the propaganda for the prevention of conception,
not because they believed it would not improve the condition of the workingman but

because they believed it would, and they plainly and loudly protested against such a possibility. They said that if the condition of the workingman should become improved by having few children he would become *verbürgerlicht,* bourgeois-like, and he would lose his revolutionary spirit (which as events have shown he did not possess at all). This was the cry repeated over and over again. [A report of that meeting appears in the third edition of the author's "Sexual Problems of To-day."]

It should not be necessary at this day to point out the shallowness of this objection. It is not the most wretched workingman that makes or gives promise of making the best revolutionist. The wretcheder the people are the wretcheder they remain. It is not the workingmen in Russia and in Spain from whom we can expect the most. On the contrary, a wretched proletariat is often a "bum" proletariat that can be used very readily for strikebreaking, for crushing the revolution, and for every dastardly kind of work, as is well known from the brutal behavior of the Black Hundreds in Russia. It is just the other way, the better the condition of the workingman the more hope of his complete awakening, because it is only the better kind of workingman who has time to read, to study, to attend meetings, to discuss things. He who is continuously overworked and underfed makes poor revolutionary timber.

Fortunately during the last few years, a decided change has been taking place in the attitude of Socialists and other radicals towards our prevention of conception propaganda and it is from them that we now get our most earnest supporters, our most zealous friends and workers.

For instance, The Woman's Page of *The New York Call,* edited by Anita C. Block, has been a staunch, outspoken and consistent supporter of our propaganda.

Chapter XVII

THE MORAL STANDARD OF THOSE WHO MAKE USE OF OR ADVOCATE THE USE OF PREVENTIVES

Philippics have been delivered and pamphlets and books have been written against those who make use of preventives and against those who advocate the rational limitation of the number of offspring. They have been called immoral, decadent, degenerate, egotists, low creatures devoid of responsibility.

It would be easy to answer by slinging epithets back at our critics and calling them fools and imbeciles incapable of logical reasoning, unwilling to be convinced and crawling into a corner when they are presented with arguments which they are unable to answer, when they are

shown proofs which they are unable to
refute. But calling names, while a great
personal satisfaction occasionally and an
excellent safety valve once in a while, is
no argument.

I will admit that among the upper
classes, and among a certain percentage
of the middle classes, the decision to limit
the number of children or to avoid having
any at all, does not flow from very high
motives, that this decision is even selfish,
egotistic in the common sense of the term,
that it flows from a desire on the part of
the parents not to have their comfort or
personal pleasures interfered with, that
they do not want to have to go thru the
trouble of bringing up children. But
this accusation is distinctly untrue when
applied to the vast majority of the middle,
professional and working classes. Far
from being due to a lower morality, it is
due to higher morality. Far from being
due to a lack of responsibility, it is due

to a heightened sense of responsibility. The animals, and the people nearest to them, have no such responsibility; they breed unrestrictedly, leaving nature or God to take care of their offspring or to kill it off as they may see fit. Thinking parents, however, are so imbued with the sense of responsibility in bringing a human being into the world under our present social and economic conditions, that we cannot blame them, but we must praise them for refusing to bring into being too large a number. As a matter of fact, it is just the other way around, and it is we who would have a perfect right, if we were so inclined, to accuse the opponents of the rational limitation of offspring among the poor of moral strabismus, of disingenuousness, of hypocrisy.

For those opponents of the artificial limitation of offspring are generally not even sincere, and cry out against the employment of it by others, while making use of it themselves. You will find that the doctors, statesmen, clergymen who weep such bitter tears over the diminished birth rate are themselves the greatest offenders in this respect, generally having few or no children. I had this experience more than once: In a discussion following one of my lectures, the man who would attack my ideas most severely would at the close of the meeting come up and ask me to have the kindness to tell him what I considered the best method of prevention. When I would ask him smilingly what he, being such an opponent of prevention, wanted it for, the answer would usually be: "Oh, well, I might as well know. There are occasions when such knowledge might be very useful." Yes, it is remarkable how many people who condemn prevention of conception on general principles are willing to utilize this knowledge for themselves, their immediate families and relatives.

Old Bacon said something to the effect that the wolf never cared how many the sheep may be and Prof. Thomas Nixon Carver of Harvard expressed the same thought very neatly as follows:

He said: "Foxes think large families among the rabbits highly commendable. Employers who want large supplies of cheap labor, priests who want large numbers of parishioners, military leaders who want plenty of cheap food for gunpowder, and politicians who want plenty of voters, all agree in commending large families and rapid multiplication among the poorer classes."

Chapter XVIII

WHAT LIFE MEANS AT PRESENT TO THE
MILLIONS

I am not an extremist, I do not take one stratum of society, namely the lowest, and try to make believe that all humanity is as wretched as that lowest stratum. I always pride myself on my sane and well-balanced radicalism, and I am certainly not a pessimist. To me personally Fate has not been particularly cruel, in fact many think that it has been particularly kind. I am distinctly an optimist. I believe that this world is going to be the most glorious world to live in and there will not be an unhappy creature in it, but to assert that this is the best of all possible worlds at the present time, is to make a statement which is stupidly, palpably

false.   Its falseness can be proven in five
minutes by going outside into the street
and just looking about us.

I know that there is plenty of joy,
plenty of happiness, plenty of pleasure
in this world, but isn't it true that the pain
overbalances the pleasure in this world
many thousand fold?   Is it not true that
we have many millions of working people
in our country who have really nothing
to live for, working from morning to night
merely for their material necessities,
merely to keep body and soul together,
but without any refining influences, without any artistic or intellectual pleasures?
Is it really reprehensible for a working
family that earns eighteen or twenty dollars a week to refuse to have more than two
children, because they know that if they
have more than two the first two will have
to be neglected to a certain extent, and to a
certain extent will have to be deprived of
food and clothes which they need?   Could

you blame them even if they refused to
have any children, because having no
pleasures whatever in life, disgusted at the
continual, monotonous drudgery of their
work, they refuse to bring other creatures
into the world that would have to live the
same cheerless, hopeless life?

What inducement is there for the intelligent class-conscious workman, holding a twelve or twenty dollar job, or having to hunt for a job half of the time, to
bring more wage-slaves into the world?
And talk to the really intelligent middle
class or professional man, the man who
has learned to look at the world with clear
eyes. You will find that he complains as
bitterly, some of them even more bitterly,
than does the workman. Until twenty-
five or twenty-eight he has to prepare for
a career. With our increased educational
requirements the age at which professional
men graduate and begin to earn a living
is advancing further and further from

year to year. For ten or fifteen years it is a bitter, hard, sixteen- or eighteen-hour a day struggle to build up a practice, to get a clientele, or to build up an independent business. And in this desperate struggle nine-tenths fail, and lead to the end of their days the lives of drudges, just merely making a living. About ten per cent. come out victorious, get to the top; but when they have reached the top they find by looking at the family Bible that they are already forty-five or fifty years old, that they are already on the decline, or will approach it within very few years, and that the material independence, position, fame, etc., do not give them the same pleasure and satisfaction that they expected to enjoy when they were struggling for them so ceaselessly and perhaps so relentlessly.

That there are a few people who seem to have been born with silver spoons in their mouths, for whom everything is prepared, who have nothing to struggle for, and to whom life seems to be an inexhaustible source of fun and pleasure, I admit. But their number is so small as to be entirely negligible, and is much more, is a thousand times, overbalanced by the men and women on the other end of the scale to whom life is a continuous source of suffering, pain, nay agony and torture, from the very day they are born until they are put away in a cheap pine coffin in the bosom of dear mother earth.

I believe that to become convinced that this is not the best possible of worlds, and that for many millions of people this life is nothing but a round of monotonous, senseless drudgery even if devoid of actual pain and suffering, it is only necessary to take a trip, not to the slums, but just in the subway, during rush hours. I thank my fates that it is but very seldom that I have to ride in the subway, but when I do, particularly if in the rush hours, the

spectacle fills me with inexpressible sad-
ness.

Just look at the faces—not a happy,
contented face in the ten cars of the express train. Just analyze them. Tense,
gloomy, dissatisfied, grouchy, distinctly
unhappy, cruel, stupid or vapid, such are
the expressions of practically all the faces
you see there. And what are they all doing there? For what reason are they
jostling or being jostled, crushing or being crushed, trampled or being trampled
upon, twice a day, morning and night of
every week-day? For what reason? To
go down into factories or shops or offices
to do useless and disagreeable, or useful
but uncongenial, or in general injurious
work for eight or ten or twelve hours a
day. And what for? Merely to make
eight or ten or twenty dollars a week, just
to support the body sufficiently to be able
to work again. It is work to have what
to eat and drink, and eat and drink to be

able to work.   And this grind goes on day after day, week after week, year after year, without any prospect of change for millions of people.

It is to me one of the great tragedies of our present system that people have to spend almost, if not the entire day, merely to earn enough to make a living. The work necessary to make a living should be the incidental work, and it certainly should not take away more than four hours a day from any man or woman. Of course, if a man loves his work that is another matter. Then he may work eighteen hours a day until his eyes close in sleep from sheer exhaustion.

And as we look across the Atlantic, as we contemplate the horrible carnage there is going on in Europe, as we consider the cruel insanity into which millions of people have been plunged, as we think of the hundreds of thousands of peaceful, healthy men departing for the front

never to return or to return maimed and
diseased, as we cast our physical and mental eyes over the fields and trenches filled
with corpses of what but recently was the
best—physically at least—of manhood—
when we see and ponder these things, how
can one dare to urge intelligent men and
women to breed unrestrainedly, to bring
forth children, to rear them, to educate
them only to become food for shell and
shrapnel, to become fertilizer for the
ground at the age of twenty or thirty?

No, this is not a pleasant world to live
in at the present time, and it is a sign of
a putrid morality and a petrified mentality to curse and to throw stones at those
members of the middle and working classes
who believe that it is their duty to themselves, to their children, to humanity at
large, to limit the number of their offspring within narrow bounds.   FAR FROM
BEING A SIGN OF LOW MORALITY THE CON-
SCIOUS CONTROL OF THE NUMBER OF CHIL-

DREN IS A SIGN OF HIGH MORALITY.   And I
will repeat what I said before, that far
from being a sign of a lack of responsibility it is a sign of a high sense of responsibility, of foresight, of love, of the true feeling of humanitarianism.

THE EVILS OF IGNORANCE AND THE BENEFITS OF KNOWLEDGE OF HARMLESS PREVENTIVES

Having answered all objections, all that I found in books or that I ever heard in discussions following my lectures on the subject, I will now present the positive side, the case for prevention.

I will summarize briefly what evils ignorance of the means of prevention and excessive childbearing is responsible for, and what benefits would accrue to humanity if the knowledge of prevention became universal, or at least universally accessible.

Chapter XIX

WOULD ENCOURAGE EARLY MARRIAGE

The reason many men marry now at such a late age is because they are afraid they would not be able to support a wife with many children. If the men knew that by safe and harmless means they could limit their children to the number they can afford to have and to a time most convenient, they would marry much earlier and more of them would marry; and this would necessarily have a great effect in diminishing the number of bachelors and old maids. This would in its turn have a great effect in diminishing prostitution with its terrible concomitant evil, venereal disease.

I am not so optimistic as to believe that early marriages and the knowledge of pre-

vention of conception will do away altogether with prostitution. People who
have studied the subject know that among
the patrons of prostitutes married men—
and happily married men, too—constitute
quite a large contingent. Patronage of
prostitutes or seeking after illicit relations
emanates from a different source than a
mere desire for sexual gratification. But
none the less it cannot be denied that if
early marriage became a common thing,
and if the fear of impregnating one's wife
were eliminated, the greatest part of the
demand for prostitution would be cut off.
And with the diminution of prostitution
goes *pari passu* a diminution in venereal
disease.

Early marriage would have other beneficial effects; it would diminish masturbation, and would tend to diminish the evils
of abstinence, neurasthenia and various
other neuroses. But these points can
only be alluded to in this book.

woman may happen to be suffering with. He forgets the horrible agony of the process of childbirth (which in spite of twilight sleep we will still have with us for quite some time to come). He forgets the dangers of hemorrhage, of lacerations, infections, puerperal convulsions. He overlooks the troubles connected with the nursing of the child, with the involution of the uterus, etc., etc.

Let us remind our dear masculine friends that in spite of the tremendous progress we have made in science, in spite of the great improvements in obstetrics and gynecology, the whole process of childbirth is still something which many women look at quite justly with some dread. Not only have the processes of gestation, labor, the puerperium and lactation quite some morbidity but they have a quite respectable or even sinister mortality. Tho the joke is not a particularly brilliant one, still it will bear repetition;

it is to the effect, that if nature had made it so that the man should have the first child and the woman the second, and thus further in alternation, there would never be a third child. If man had to go thru what women do, if men were not only the begetters but also the bearers of children, the laws against the prevention of conception on our statute books would never have been put on, or if they had been put on they would have been very quickly taken off.

Often in the discussions following my lectures a man would get up and would attempt to refute my argument by the statement that he has had six or eight or ten children and that his wife was perfectly healthy, and that they had no trouble, and that the children all grew up well and are a joy and pleasure to them. But on investigating it has proved invariably that the objector was a very well-to-do or rich man, and that his wife could afford all possible comforts, that each child had a nurse, the girls had governesses, etc. The attempted refutation, it is clearly seen, will hold no water. I have never urged the rich and well-to-do to limit the number of their children. Under our present conditions let them have as many as they wish, but what is easy, feasible and even pleasurable for a rich couple may be extremely depressing and painful for the poor or the middle class business or professional man, and it is for them that I am pleading.

Chapter XXII

KILLS THE WOMAN'S SPIRIT

Besides the deleterious effect that frequent childbearing has upon the health of the woman, often making her prematurely aged and often hastening her death, there is another point to be considered. It cripples or kills the spirit of many a woman. Who has not known of high spirited, high-strung girls with talent for music, painting, singing, acting or writing, who in a few years after marriage have become spiritless drudges without any hope and without any ambition?

Of course a husband alone may be the cause of such a condition; an uncongenial or unsympathetic husband may without any outside "aid" succeed in a very short time in completely crushing and maiming the best woman's spirit and aspirations. But in the vast majority of cases it will be found that the real cause of this metamorphosis is the children or pregnancies following closely upon each other. How can a woman who has four or five children within the first ten years of her married life ever think of following up her studies and living up to her ideals and aspirations?

This argument will not appeal to many men, who think that that is all a woman is for—to breed children, that once she has entered into the holy bonds of matrimony she must like those entering Dante's inferno leave everything behind and devote herself exclusively to the business of being a mother. I, however, do not agree with the notions of those estimable members of my sex. I believe that a woman is, can be and should be a human being besides being a mother, and if she is to take a place in and get some enjoyment out of her individual and social life, she must not be forced to be a breeding machine merely.

Chapter XXIII

NEURASTHENIA IN MEN AND WOMEN FROM IMPROPER METHODS

On account of our vicious laws, which prevent a free discussion of preventives and which make the imparting of knowledge on the subject so difficult, many women use improper and injurious methods of prevention and thereby injure their health or risk their very lives. Were a free discussion of the subject permissible this evil would be done away with.

Similarly there are numberless thousands of men who have become pitiable weaklings, pitiable sexual neurasthenics, from coitus interruptus, or from other injurious methods which they practice thru ignorance of better and harmless methods of prevention. Universal knowledge of the proper means of contraception would save these men from a deplorable fate, would do away with an evil which is greatly on the increase.

Chapter XXIV

LARGELY RESPONSIBLE FOR THE ABORTION EVIL

This is one of the most important points in our discussion. The evil of abortion is one of the most terrible evils in our society. It kills thousands of unmarried and tens of thousands of married women. If it does not kill, it often infects, maims and weakens for life. The public will never know just exactly how many victims are sacrificed yearly to the terrible Moloch. For, to the honor of the medical profession, be it said, that the physician who is called in to treat a girl or woman dying from a criminal abortion, very often at great risk to himself, protects the good name of the poor woman, and does not give on the death certificate the true cause of death. And whenever I hear of a case of a woman dying from an abortion, as I do not infrequently, I blame not the woman—on the contrary, my heart goes out in pity to the poor victim of our brutal laws—but my blood boils with indignation at society or the State, which mercilessly and pitilessly sacrifices every year so many of its

mothers. The knowledge of the prevention of conception would do away entirely
with the evil of abortion, or would reduce
it at least to a minimum. Every investi-
gator has found that wherever means of
prevention of conception are most difficult
to obtain, there abortions are at their highest. Where preventives are easy to obtain, where their sale is permitted by law,
there both abortion and illegitimacy are
reduced to a minimum.

Chapter XXV

WOULD DIMINISH PROSTITUTION IN MARRIED LIFE

We know that a good many married
men who patronize prostitution do so not
on account of wickedness merely, but to
a great extent they are driven to it by the
fear of impregnating their wives. And
what is more—and this is an illuminating

commentary on our pitiful social conditions—many wives know it and not only
say nothing, but actually encourage their
husbands to visit prostitutes, only to leave
them alone, such is their terror of another
and another and another pregnancy.
Only recently I read in a German publication that it is not an infrequent occurrence among the lower classes in Germany
for the wife who earns her own money to
give a part of it to the husband in order
that he may go to other women and leave
her alone.   What this means in increased
risks of venereal disease needs no detailed
discussion.   A knowledge of the means of
prevention would obviate this terrible evil.
Not only our sanitarians but our moralists
who care more for a man's soul than for
his body, should from this point of view
alone be in favor of prevention.

Chapter XXVI

THE ENORMOUS BENEFITS OF PREVENTION OF CONCEPTION FROM THE EUGENIC STANDPOINT

We now come to another extremely important point. The word eugenics is on the lips of every one, people who know what it means and people who have the most fantastic notions as to the purport of eugenics and what the eugenists stand for. We know perfectly well that there are people whom it is a crime to permit to bring children into the world. About the unquestionably insane, imbeciles, morons, and perverts, we need not worry in this respect. Society will have to take care of them by sterilizing them or segregating them. But there are people who can very well get married, provided they do not bring children into the world. Among such we may mention people suffering with tuberculosis, epilepsy, perhaps cancer and certain mental abnormalities. We have no right to deprive those people of any affection in their lives. And besides, it would be worse than useless to do so. If you raise the barriers for entering matrimony too high, if you make your requirements for a marriage certificate too rigid, those people will be sure to enter into illicit unions, and this means an enormous increase in prostitution and illegitimacy, two undoubted evils. But teach those people the proper means of prevention of conception and the problem is solved. For of one thing we may be sure: Leaving out of consideration the imbeciles, morons and degenerates who could not be taught to use any precautionary measures, and whom, as I said before, society will have to protect itself against in a different way, there are no parents who would deliberately bring children into the world whom they had reason to fear would be tainted with hereditary disease. No sane parents wish to bring into the world handicapped, maimed and deformed children.

What I said just now also applies to thousands of syphilitics. There are thousands of syphilitic men and women who are perfectly safe as far as their partner is concerned, but are not safe enough to become parents. They cannot infect but they must not give birth to children for fear that the children may have the taint in them. The use of preventives settles this problem and saves the world from thousands of pitiable hereditary syphilitics.

Or is it better to permit tainted parents to bring syphilitic, epileptic and insane children into the world than to use preventives? One reverend gentleman who criticised my teachings said that it was. He said it was much better to have the streets full of syphilitic, maimed and defective children than to accept the doctrines of Dr. Robinson.

And in speaking of the subject of hereditary syphilis I cannot refrain from mentioning a case that I saw but a few days ago. It was the young mother's fifth child. The first two children were born dead, the third and fourth died very soon after birth, and at last the distressed and unsophisticated mother was overjoyed at giving birth to a child that lived. The child is a year and a half old now. It would have been better for it and for society if it had been born dead or died soon after birth—much better, of course, if it had never been conceived. For it was one of the most pitiable, one of the most sickening objects that we are called to look upon in our practice. I know of no more pitiable spectacle than a baby suffering with hereditary syphilis. This child was full of sores and ulcers, the lip was eaten away, it had the characteristic syphilitic snuffles, breathing loudly and with great difficulty, in short it was a pitiable sight. The cause of all this misery is the brutal father. The mother has, of course, also become syphilitic.

Now what are you going to do with that couple? Tell them to abstain? Just try to make such a brute abstain. He would simply go to another woman, infecting right and left. The only way you could make him abstain is by locking him up in jail. If you cannot do that, then in the name of decency and common sense teach such couples, of which there are thousands in our broad land, at least not to bring any more wretched, diseased creatures into the world.

Then again there are thousands of women who suffer from diseases which are not hereditary, which are not dangerous in themselves, but become dangerous only when pregnancy occurs. Such are cases of advanced heart or kidney disease, cases of very narrow or deformed pelvis, cases of tendencies to eclampsia or puerperal convulsions. As long as these women do not become pregnant they get along very well. To impregnate them means to aggravate their disease, to hasten their end or actually to drive them into the grave. As I have to tell many a time to some men, to impregnate their wives would be equivalent to murder. The knowledge of the prevention of conception would obviate these potential murders.

Many more arguments could be adduced, but I believe even with the points I have presented so far, the case for prevention is impossible to refute or demolish. I therefore feel perfectly justified in repeating and concluding with my well-known motto, namely that: There is no single measure that would so positively, so immediately, contribute toward the happiness and progress of the human race as teaching the people the proper means of prevention of conception.

Chapter XXVII

PREVENTION OF CONCEPTION AND ABORTION

To this point to which I alluded before I must devote a separate chapter; for the greatest obstacle we meet in our prevention of conception propaganda is the confusion, both on the part of physicians and on the part of the laity, of prevention of conception with abortion.

Just as the statute books speak of the two in the same sentence, meting out the same severe punishment for both, so the physician and the layman often speak of the two as if they were one and the same thing practically, as if the one were as objectionable or as criminal as the other, and as if believing in the one necessarily meant accepting the other.

131

This almost universally prevalent confusion is, as I said, one of the greatest obstacles in the spread of the prevention of conception propaganda, and it is important to clarify this confusion and to shed some light on the subject. Not only do contraception and abortion not belong in the same category, but I can truthfully say that one of the principal reasons, one of the strongest motives that makes us advocate contraception so persistently and so assiduously is because we want to do away with the evil of abortion as far as we can; for we do consider abortion a terrible evil.

Not being engaged in the lucrative practice of the abortionist, I am free to speak of the subject calmly and frankly and am not under obligation to become hysterical in condemning it publicly as are many of those who are practicing it secretly. I say frankly and boldly that there are cases, many cases, in which not

to induce an abortion is much more cowardly, much more cruel, much more dis-
honest, than it would be to induce one.
The peace of mind, the honor, the very
life itself, and not only of one person but
of several persons, very often depend
upon the artificial emptying of the uterus.
And under our present social and economic conditions the professional abortionist, much as we may despise or condemn him, has more than once proved a
real benefactor, in saving the sanity, the
health and the life of a frantic young
woman and her frantic family.

But admitting all that, I still consider
abortion a real, a serious evil. It is de-
grading and humiliating to the woman.
It is always accompanied with some risk,
if not to the life at least to the health of
the person (tho the dangers of the operation when performed under proper conditions have been greatly diminished, they
have not yet been entirely eliminated and

it is a question if they ever will be) and it is apt to lead to abuses. For this and various other reasons all true humanitarians are endeavoring to do everything possible to diminish the evil of abortion, which is constantly on the increase. And one of the most effective remedies to diminish the evil is the universal knowledge of the proper means of prevention of conception.

And just as it is disgraceful for our statute books to speak of prevention and abortion in the same sentence, meting out the same punishment to both, so it is disgraceful for any physician to get up and talk of the two in the same breath as if they belonged to the same category.

Doesn't any person with any sense see that the two are entirely different, not only in degree but in kind? In inducing abortion we destroy something already formed; we destroy a fetus or an embryo, a fertilized ovum, a potential human being.   In prevention, however, we merely prevent chemically or mechanically the spermatozoa from coming in contact with the ovum.   There is no greater crime or sin in this than there is in simple abstinence, in refraining from sexual intercourse.

And while everybody is, of course, entitled to his opinions and anybody may entertain any opinions on the subject of prevention that he chooses, nobody has a right to confuse the issues and speak of prevention and abortion as if they were the same or similar things.   And I trust that in the future our esteemed opponents will bear this point in mind, will endeavor to be more honest and will not, either ignorantly or maliciously, confuse the issues.

CHAPTER XXVIII.

THE OBJECT OF THIS BOOK.
AN ANSWER TO ILL-ADVISED CRITICISM.

Some people on reading or glancing thru this book, and finding no actual description of the means for preventing conception feel rather disappointed at the omission of what is to them the most important point. They believe that the book should give a list of prevenceptives and describe in detail the means and methods.

Now, anybody who expects to find in a book circulated in this country the actual means for preventing conception, shows a naiveté, an ignorance, which is simply exasperating. If prevenceptive information could be freely circulated, no books on birth control would be necessary or would find any readers. No birth control movement would be called for. No birth control organizations would have to fight and struggle to advocate voluntary parenthood, no birth control advocates would be arrested, no Herculean efforts would be required to attempt to abrogate the laws against imparting prevenceptive information. The knowledge of prevenception would be common knowledge and every adult would possess it.

But just because the spread of prevenceptive knowledge, the giving of actual means of prevenception, is a criminal offense, punishable by five years in prison and a $5,000 fine, it is necessary that such books be written and circulated as widely as possible.

Some people say: "Oh, we know birth control is all right. We fully agree with it, but what we want is the actual means."

You may know of birth control and agree that it is right, but there are millions and millions of men and women who are utterly indifferent to the question and there are other millions who fight any attempt at the spread of the birth control propaganda and there are still other millions *who do not know that there is such a thing* in the world as birth control. They have no idea that means of prevention of conception exist. They are pleasurably shocked and surprised when they first find out there is a possibility of controling the number of offspring and that women do not have to go on having children, year after year, during their entire reproductive period.

It is to fight the ignorance, the indifference and the actual antagonism that books like this are necessary, and if you are not narrowly selfish, if you have not bought the book merely for the purpose of helping yourself, if you have some interest in the welfare of your neighbors, of your community, of the nation, and of the human race as a whole, it is your sacred duty not only to become thoroly familiar with all the arguments for birth control, but to spread the propaganda far and wide. There is no hope for mankind until it learns to control its birthrate.

Chapter XXIX

THE LAWS AGAINST PREVENCEPTION IN THE VARIOUS STATES IN THE UNION.

Not all States have the same laws regarding prevenceptive information. Some states are more liberal than others. The Federal law applies of course to every State in the Union, but it applies only to information sent by mail or by express from one State to another. It does not apply to verbal information or to information given by one person to another within the same State.

Twenty-four States (and Porto Rico) specifically and distinctly penalize the imparting of prevenceptive knowledge. Those states are: Arizona, California, Colorado, Connecticut, Idaho, Indiana, Iowa, Kansas, Maine, Massachusetts, Minnesota, Mississippi, Missouri, Montana, Nebraska, Nevada, New Jersey, New York, North Dakota, Ohio, Oklahoma, Pennsylvania, Washington, Wyoming and Porto Rico.

But twenty-four States *have no specific laws against imparting prevenceptive information*. They have obscenity laws under which, on account of Federal Statutes, prevenceptive knowledge may be classed as "obscene", but the laws do not mention prevenceptive information specifically and there is no doubt that if the Federal Statute against imparting information for the prevention of conception were repealed, no further legislation would be required in these states. These twenty-four states are: Alabama, Arkansas, Delaware, Florida, Georgia, Illinois, Kentucky, Louisiana, Maryland, Michigan, New Hampshire, New Mexico, North Carolina, Oregon, Rhode Island, South Carolina, South Dakota, Tennessee, Texas, West Virginia, Wisconsin, Virginia, Utah, Vermont, and also Alaska, Hawaii and the District of Columbia.

While, as stated, these twenty-four states have no laws against imparting this information, it is of course not known whether or not physicians, druggists, and others possibly in possession of it will be willing to furnish it.

Chapter XXX

THE LAW ON THE SUBJECT

Some people are quite unaware of the existence of any laws against the dissemination of information regarding the prevention of conception. They are the most surprised people in the world when they learn that the giving of such information is a criminal offense, punishable by fine and imprisonment. The prevention of undesirable pregnancy seems to them such a fundamental personal right, that they cannot understand how the State was ever permitted to interfere with it. Others have very vague ideas on the subject, and I have met even eminent lawyers who were in ignorance as to exact penalties prescribed by our Federal and State laws. We frequently get requests to give the exact wording of the law. I therefore publish here verbatim the United States or Federal statute, and also the statute of the State of New York.

UNITED STATES CRIMINAL CODE, SECTION 211

(Act of March 4, 1909, Chapter 321, Section 211, United States Statutes at Large, vol. 35, part 1, page 1088 et seq.) provides as follows:

"Every obscene, lewd or lascivious and every filthy book, pamphlet, picture, paper, letter, writing, print, or other publication of an indecent character, and every article or thing designated, adapted or intended for preventing conception or procuring abortion, or for any indecent or immoral use; and every article, instrument, substance, drugs, medicine, or thing which is advertised or described in a manner calculated to lead another to use or apply it for preventing conception or producing abortion, or for any indecent or immoral purpose; and every written or printed card, letter, circular, book, pamphlet, advertisement or notice of any kind giving information, directly, or

indirectly, where or how, or from whom or by
what means any of the hereinbefore mentioned
matters, articles or things may be obtained or
made, or where or by whom any act or operation of any kind for the procuring or producing of abortion will be done or performed, or
how or by what means conception may be prevented or abortion produced, whether sealed
or unsealed; and every letter, packet or pack-
age or other mail matter containing any filthy,
vile or indecent thing, device or substance; and
every paper, writing, advertisement or repre-
sentation that any article, instrument, substance, drug, medicine or thing may, or can be
used or applied for preventing conception or
producing abortion, or for any indecent or immoral purpose; and every description calculated to induce or incite a person to so use or
apply any such article, instrument, substance,
drug, medicine or thing, is hereby declared to
be non-mailable matter, and shall not be con-
veyed in the mails or delivered from any post-
office or by any letter carrier. Whoever shall
knowingly deposit, or cause to be deposited for
mailing or delivery, anything declared by this
section to be non-mailable, or shall knowingly

take, or cause the same to be taken, from the mails for the purpose of circulating or disposing thereof, or of aiding in the circulation or disposition of the same, shall be fined not more than $5,000, or imprisoned not more than five years, or both."

Note the devilish ingenuity with which this law is worded. No loophole, no hope of escape. And note the criminal asininity of putting preventing conception and procuring abortion in exactly the same category, meting out the same punishment for one as for the other. But the Federal law deals only with the penalties for imparting the information by mail. The Federal law cannot interfere with any information sent by express within the territory of a State, or imparted orally. But the laws of the various States have looked out for that. Here for instance is the law of the State of New York. Other States have similar laws, some more drastic, some milder.

An amendment to the law was passed providing the same punishment for sending the information by express.

Here for instance is the New York statute. It constitutes Section 1142 of the Penal Law and reads as follows:

"A person who sells, lends, gives away, or in any manner exhibits or offers to sell, lend or give away, or has in his possession with intent to sell, lend or give away, or advertises, or offers for sale, loan or distribution, any instrument or article, or any recipe, drug or medicine for the prevention of conception, or for causing unlawful abortion, or purporting to be for the prevention of conception, or for causing unlawful abortion, or advertises, or holds out representations that it can be so used or applied, or any such description as will be calculated to lead another to so use or apply any such article, recipe, drug, medicine or instrument, or who writes or prints, or causes to be written or printed, a card, circular, pamphlet, advertisement or notice of any kind, or gives information orally, stating when, where, how, of whom, or by what means such an instrument, article, recipe, drug or medicine can be purchased or obtained, or who manufactures any such instrument, article, recipe, drug or medicine, is guilty of a misdemeanor, and shall be liable to the same penalties as provided in section eleven hundred and forty-one of this chapter."

The punishment so provided for is a sentence of not less than ten days nor more than one year imprisonment or a fine not less than fifty dollars nor more than one thousand dollars or both fine and imprisonment for each offense.

Note again the asininity of confusing prevention of conception with abortion, of putting them in the same category and inflicting the same punishment for both, as if the two were one and the same thing.

Is it any wonder that intelligent humane men and women have the deepest contempt for these laws, are working for their abrogation, and in the meantime, have no compunction about breaking them whenever they can safely do so?

Chapter XXXI

HOW TO ABOLISH THE LAW AGAINST THE PREVENTION OF CONCEPTION

I am not in sympathy with those impatient people who object to any propaganda of ideas as "mere words, words," and demand ACTION. As a rule those are very foolish people, because words whether spoken or written are also action and prepare the ground for effective and permanent change, while action, direct action, undertaken at a time when the conditions are not ripe, when the people are not ready, simply gets the perpetrator of the action into trouble and does not accomplish anything at all.

But I do agree that we have been propagandizing sufficiently, that public opinion seems to be more favorable towards our humane ideas about limiting offspring among the poor, and we believe that the time is ripe for a fight and for a test. It is time to test our strength and see if we cannot abolish altogether the brutal laws on the statute books against the prevention of conception propaganda. If we cannot abolish them, let us at least try to make them ridiculous and ineffective.

What would be the best means of direct action? For a poor and obscure man or woman, for an extreme radical, to defy the law and to distribute circulars about prevention of conception would be very foolish, tho at the same time heroic and pathetic. But it would not accomplish anything. The man or woman would get a few months in prison and the law would still remain on our statute books to harass the physician and the layman alike, and to make an efficient propaganda among the poor—those who most need it—impossible. But there are now not a few well-to-do, well-known and influential men and women who thoroly believe that teaching the poor the means of limiting their offspring is one of the most important means of bettering their condition and of raising the racial standard. And if a few such men and women, particularly women, were willing to risk martyrdom (they would probably not have to suffer it, merely risk it) the law would quickly fall into disrepute.

I am sure that if a dozen of our rich or not rich but respected and influential women, who are thoroly in sympathy with the limitation of offspring propaganda, would undertake to distribute information, either by word of mouth or by printed circular, Anthony Comstock would not dare to arrest them. And if he were goaded into arresting them, such a howl would be raised, that the law, if not abolished, would surely fall into disrepute. And the educational value of such a trial would be enormous.

If a hundred, or fifty, or at least a dozen women in sympathy with our work would risk a little inconvenience for the sake of a great cause, they would accomplish a great deal.

Chapter XXXII

SOME QUOTATIONS

I am not a great believer in quotations from authorities. And very few of them will be found in any of my writings. For I believe that an argument should be strong enough to stand on its own bottom without props from authorities. If a thing is true, if the arguments on which it is based are logical and unanswerable, then corroborative opinions from a dozen or a hundred other men do not make it more true. And if an argument is weak, if by a little analysis its falsity, complete or partial, can be shown, then the fact that a thousand or a million people hold the same belief does not make it less false, less untenable.

If what I have said up to this point has

not convinced my readers that the volitional, rational control of offspring is a
measure of the utmost importance for the
welfare of the individual and of the race,
then the mere opinions of some great and
prominent men, who believed and believe
as I do, should not have any better success.

And still I cannot refrain from pre-
senting a few quotations. Why? Because so many people belong mentally in
the kindergarten class, and those people
are influenced more by opinions of eminent authorities than by logical, well-
sustained, unanswerable arguments. One
might say that the opinions of mental
kindergartners do not amount to much
and are not worth influencing. This
is not so. We have a right to use
all honorable methods to convert people
to our point of view, and especially
so in a republic, where the vote of a
mental infant counts for just as much as

the vote of a great thinker. And if we wish to have our laws against the prevention of conception propaganda abolished or made a dead letter, we must convert as many people as possible. In voting, unfortunately, quantity is even more important than quality. And then, on our legislators opinions of great men have an undoubted influence. Hence it is worth while to see what some of the world's good and great men think of the subject of the rational limitation of offspring.

And first of all it gives me pleasure to quote from my good and esteemed friend Dr. A. Jacobi, who in his presidential address before the American Medical Association, the largest and most influential, and also most conservative, organized body of physicians in the world, had the courage to put in a word for our limitation of offspring propaganda.

Here is what he said:

Is there no way to prevent those who are born into this world from becoming sickly both physically and mentally? It seems almost impossible as long as the riches provided by this world are accessible to a part of the living only. The resources for prevention or cure are inaccessible to many— sometimes even to a majority. That is why it has become an indispensable suggestion that *only a certain number of babies should be born into the world.* As long as not infrequently even the well-to-do limit the number of their offspring, *the advice to the poor*—or those to whom the raising of a large family is worse than merely difficult—*to limit the number of children, even the healthy ones, is perhaps more than merely excusable.* I often hear that an American family has had ten children, but only three or four survived. Before the former succumbed they were a source of expense, poverty and morbidity to the few survivors. *For the interest*

*of the latter and the health of the com-
munity at large, they had better not have
been born.*

And here is what another president, the
President of the British Medical Associa-
tion, said in his presidential address at
Liverpool on July 23, 1912:

We have successfully interfered with
the selective death-rate which Nature employed in eliminating the unfit, but, on the
other hand, we have made no serious attempt to establish a selective birthrate so
as to prevent the race being carried on
by the least worthy citizens. The same
maudlin sentimentality which often per-
vades the public not infrequently infects
the medical profession. We have often
joined forces with self-constituted moralists in denouncing the falling birth-rate,
and have called out for quantity regardless
of quality. . . . We readily forget that
utility, as long ago pointed out by John

Stuart Mill, lies at the basis of all morality.   We are also apt to forget that a high
birth-rate is practically always associated
with a high death-rate, and a low birth-
rate with a low death-rate; the former is
Nature's method, a method which has always produced a fine race, tho very slow
in doing so; but, with the advance of civilization, Nature's method is too cruel and
barbarous, and, as Man rises superior to
Nature and obtains more and more control
over her laws, such barbarities are replaced
by more humane methods.

I know that in the expression of these
views I am coming into direct conflict with
at least some of the Churches, of which
there are almost as many varieties as there
are of human beings.   The majority preach
in favor of quantity rather than quality;
they advocate a high birth-rate regardless
of the consequences, and boldly tell you
that it is better to be born an imbecile than
not to have been born at all.   They forget

the saying of Jesus of Nazareth that it
would have been well for this man if he had
never been born. With the man-made
morality of the Church I can have neither
art nor part. There must be a high racial
morality based on utility and the greatest
happiness not merely of the individual but
of the race. Medical men, when they are
consulted, as they often are, on questions
of matrimony and reproduction incur a
very serious responsibility when they encourage the mating of mental and physical
weaklings. It is their duty not to pander
to the selfish gratification of the individual, but to point out to every one his positive and negative duties to the race.

One of the world's greatest thinkers and
philosophers, John Stuart Mill, was a very
ardent believer in the principle of the artificial limitation of offspring. Here is
what he says in his "Principles of Political Economy" (Book II, Chapter xii):

Every one has a right to live. We will suppose this granted. But no one has a right to bring creatures into life to be supported by other people. Whoever means to stand upon the first of these rights must renounce all pretensions to the last. If a man cannot support even himself unless others help him, those others are entitled to say that they do not also undertake the support of any offspring which it is physically possible for him to summon into the world. Yet there are abundance of writers and public speakers, including many of the most ostentatious pretentions to high feeling, whose views of life are so truly brutish that they see hardship in preventing paupers from breeding hereditary paupers in the workhouse itself. Posterity will one day ask with astonishment, what sort of people it could be among whom such preachers could find proselytes.

It would be possible for the State to guarantee employment, at ample wages, to all who are born. But if it does this, it is bound in self-protection and for the sake of every purpose for which government exists, to provide that no person shall be born without its consent. If the ordinary and spontaneous motives to self-restraint are removed others must be substituted. Restrictions on marriage, at least equivalent to those existing in some of the German States, or severe penalties on those who have children when unable to support them, would then be indispensable. Society can feed the necessitous, if it takes their multiplication under its control; or (if destitute of all moral feeling for the wretched offspring) it can leave the last to their discretion, abandoning the first to their own care. But it cannot with impunity take the feeding upon itself, and leave the multiplying free.

Prof. Huxley, than whom no keener thinker ever lived, stated it as his opinion that:

So long as unlimited multiplication goes on, no social organization which has ever been devised, no fiddle-faddling with the distribution of wealth, will deliver society from the tendency to be destroyed by the reproduction within itself, in its intensest form, of that struggle for existence, the limitation of which is the object of society.

The Population Question is the real riddle of the Sphinx. In view of the ravages of the terrible monster Over-Multiplication, all other riddles sink into insignificance.

I will conclude with the remarks of a man whom I consider one of the sanest and clearest thinkers in the English speaking world. I refer to H. G. Wells. I consider him the ideal type of radical.

While not afraid to go to the very root of every question, while no subject is too sacred to him for free and frank discussion, he does not slop over, he does not cut himself off from the rest of mankind, refusing to do anything because he cannot do everything; he knows that half a loaf is better than no bread, and he recognizes the important fact that if we want to accomplish anything we must take humanity as it is and not as we should like it to be. He is less brilliant and less scintillating than George Bernard Shaw, but the brain of the latter is a complete muddle on many subjects, he will often sacrifice the truth to a *bon mot* or an epigram, and his flippancy and clownishness are sometimes— especially in times that stir men's souls— repellant. But H. G. Wells can always be relied upon to say what he has to say in a trenchant, logical manner. He is a true humanitarian and, I repeat, the ideal type of radical, tho of course it does not mean

that I agree with all of his ideas and conclusions.   And here is what Wells has to
say on the subject of this book in his "An-
ticipations":

For a multitude of contemptible and
silly creatures, fear-driven and helpless
and useless, unhappy or hatefully happy
in the midst of squalid dishonor, feeble,
ugly, inefficient, born of unrestrained
lusts, and increasing and multiplying
thru sheer incontinence and stupidity, the
men of the New Republic will have little
pity and less benevolence.   To make life
convenient for the breeding of such people
will seem to them not the most virtuous
and amiable thing in the world, as it is
held to be now, but an exceedingly abom-
inable proceeding.   Procreation is an
avoidable thing for sane persons of even
the most furious passions, and the men of
the New Republic will hold that the procreation of children who, by the circumstances of their parentage, *must* be dis-

eased bodily and mentally—I do not think
it will be difficult for the medical science
of the coming time to define such circumstances—is absolutely the most loathsome
of all conceivable sins. They will hold, I
anticipate, that a certain portion of the
population—the small minority, for example, afflicted with indisputably transmissible diseases, with transmissible mental disorders, with such hideous incurable
habits of mind as the craving for intoxi-
cation—exists only on sufferance, out of
pity and patience, and on the understand-
ing that they do not propagate; . . .

St. Paul tells us that it is better to
marry than to burn, but to beget children
on that account will appear, I imagine, to
these coming men as an absolutely loathsome proceeding. They will stifle no
spread of knowledge that will diminish
their swarming misery of childhood in the
slums, they will regard the disinclination
of the artless "Society" woman to become

a mother as a most amiable trait in her folly. . . . Most of the human types, that by civilized standards are undesirable, are quite willing to die out thru such suppressions if the world will only encourage them a little. They multiply in sheer ignorance, but they do not desire multiplication even now, and they could easily be made to dread it. . . .

The inevitable removal of births from the sphere of an uncontrollable Providence to the category of deliberate acts will enormously enhance the responsibility of the parent—and of the State that has failed to adequately discourage the philoprogenitiveness of the parent—towards the child. Having permitted the child to come into existence, public policy and the older standard of justice alike demand, under these new conditions, that it must be fed, cherished and educated, not merely up to a respectable minimum, but to the full height of its possibilities. The State will, therefore, be the reserve guardian of all children. If they are being under-nourished, if their education is being neglected, the state will step in, take over the responsibility of their management, and enforce their charge upon the parents.

Those are splendid words which should be gravely pondered over by our reformers (and would-be reformers), philanthropists, sociologists and legislators.

Other opinions on the subject, among them those of Herbert Spencer, will be found in Dr. Jacobi's article, in the Articles from *The Critic and Guide*.

And I will conclude these quotations with the words of an eminent judge. Our judges are very conservative, are influenced by precedent, and when they see that one of their own class was in favor of our propaganda, they may be more inclined to give us a hearing, and—who knows?—may perhaps even show leniency to one who may be unfortunate enough to fall into the clutches of the law.

In the year 1888, when Mrs. Annie Besant's "Law of Population" was prosecuted in Australia, Mr. Justice Windeyer, in a judgment delivered in the Supreme Court of New South Wales, most strongly upheld the book as necessary and valuable. The following is an extract from this judgment:

"A court of law has now to decide for the first time whether it is lawful to argue in a decent way with earnestness of thought and sobriety of language the right of married men and women to limit the number of children to be begotten by them by such means as medical science says are possible and not injurious to health. Of the enormous importance of this question, not only to persons of limited means in every society and country, but to nations, the populations of which have a tendency to increase more rapidly than the means

of subsistence, there cannot be the slightest doubt. Since the days when Malthus
first announced his views on the subject to
be misrepresented and vilified, as orig-
inators of new ideas usually are by the
ignorant and unthinking, the question has
not only been pressing itself with increasing intensity of force upon thinkers and
social reformers dealing with it in the abstract, but the necessity of practically
dealing with the difficulty of over-population has become a topic publicly discussed
by statesmen and politicians. It is no
longer a question whether it is expedient
to prevent the growth of a pauper population, with all its attendant miseries following upon semi-starvation, overcrowd-
ing, disease, and an enfeebled national
stamina of constitution; but how countries
suffering from all these causes of national
decay shall avert national disaster by
checking the production of children, whose
lives must be too often a misery to them-

selves, a burden to society, and a danger to the State. Public opinion has so far advanced in the consideration of a question that has become of burning importance in the mother country by reason of its notoriously increasing over-population, that invectives are no longer hurled against those who, like John Stuart Mill and others, discuss in the abstract the necessity of limiting the growth of population; but they are reserved for those who attempt practically to follow up their teaching and show how such abstract reasoning should be acted upon.   It seems to be conceded by public opinion, and has indeed been admitted in argument before us, that the abstract discussion of the necessity of limiting the number of children brought into the world is a subject fitted for the philosopher and student of sociology. The thinkers of the world have so far succeeded in educating it upon the subject, and public attention is so thoroly aroused as to its importance, that every reader of our English periodical literature knows it to be constantly discussed in magazines and reviews. Statesmen, reviewers, and ecclesiastics join in a common chorus of exhortation against improvident marriages to the working class, and preach to them the necessity of deferring the ceremony till they have saved the competency necessary to support the truly British family of ten or twelve children. Those, however, who take a practical view of life, will inevitably ask whether the masses, for whose benefit this exhortation is given, can be expected to exercise all the powers of self-denial which compliance with earning his three or four shillings a day, without any hope of ever being able to educate, and bring up eight or ten children would demand? The Protestant world rejects the idea of a celibate clergy as incompatible with purity and the safety of female virtue, tho the ecclesiastic is strengthened by all the moral helps of a calling devoted to the noblest of objects, and by every inducement to a holy life. With strange inconsistence, the same disbelievers in the power of male human nature to resist the most powerful instincts, expect men and women, animated by no such exalted motives, with their moral nature more or less stunted, huddled together in dens where the bare conditions of living preclude even elementary ideas of modesty, with none of the pleasures of life, save those enjoyed in common with the animals—expect these victims of a social state, for which the educated are responsible if they do not use their superior wisdom and knowledge for its redress, to exercise all the self-control of which the celibate ecclesiastic is supposed to be incapable. If it is right to declaim against over-population as a danger to society, as involving conditions of life not only destructive to morals but conclusive to crime and national degeneration, the question immediately arises, can it be wrong to discuss the possibility of limiting births by methods which do not involve in their application the existence of an impossible state of society in the world as it is, and which do not ignore the natural sexual instincts in man.

"Why is the philosopher who describes the nature of the diseases from which we are suffering, who detects the causes which induce it and the general character of the remedies to be applied, to be regarded as a sage and a benefactor, but his necessary complement in the evolution of a great idea, the man who works out in practice the theories of the abstract thinker, to be denounced as a criminal?"

ARTICLES FROM
THE CRITIC AND GUIDE

THE CRITIC AND GUIDE AND ITS PROPAGANDA

The Critic and Guide was the first journal in this country to advocate the rational limitation of offspring and to demand the abrogation of the laws against imparting information about the prevention of conception. It still remains the only journal in its field. There is hardly an issue which does not contain one or several editorials and articles dealing with the subject from various points of view.

When we started our propaganda, there was not a publication, either medical or lay, that could be induced to touch the subject however mildly, however gingerly. Any discussion of it, either pro or con, was in the literal sense of the word, taboo. It was considered indecent, obscene to refer to it. (A question which concerns the very life and happiness of the individual and of the race indecent!) Fortunately, our persistent propaganda has had its effect. There are now several publications that

venture occasionally to allude to the subject.
They still do it in a timid, apologetic manner;
some bring it up only to condemn it in the most
approved medieval fashion, but still the taboo
has been broken, and the writer hopes that this
volume will serve to still further influence, in
the right direction, the editorial thought of the
country.

Of the numerous articles on the subject of
prevention of conception which appeared in
The Critic and Guide the following present the
subjects from slightly different angles perhaps,
and will serve to complement what we have had
to say.   The man who fails to be convinced by
the arguments presented by us and by those
that follow is hopeless indeed.   He will never
be a convert to our cause.

A COUNTRY IN WHICH THE PREVENTION OF CONCEPTION IS OFFICIALLY SANCTIONED

By Dr. J. Rutgers, The Hague, Holland.

[I was extremely glad to learn that we have at least one country in the world in which the prevention of conception is legally sanctioned, a country which is doing exactly what I have been advocating for many years should be done, namely that physicians and visiting nurses should instruct the people in the methods of prevention and furnish these means free to the poor—and in which the results are exactly as I foretold they would be, namely the general health of the people has improved, the mortality has fallen down to the lowest in Europe, illegitimate births have decreased, sexual "immorality" has not increased, and poverty and various forms of degeneracy are decidedly on the decrease. Foreigners are generally apt to magnify the value of the good things they find in another country, and I therefore asked Dr. J.

Rutgers of The Hague, one of the most indefatigable workers in the cause of limitation of offspring among the poor, to give me a brief statement of just what exactly the free neomalthusian propaganda has accomplished in Holland. He wrote the statement for me in English, and I reproduce it in his own words with merely a few stylistic corrections here and there.]

The kingdom of Holland, which in former centuries had fought itself free from the clerical government of Spain, is perhaps the only country in the world where freedom of speech and press is not a fiction.* Apart from criminal and obscene publications every opinion is admissible by law and by post. Limitation of offspring is as freely discussed as artificial fecundation. Conscious regulation of one's offspring in accordance with one's existing means for living and for education, in accord-

---

* In 1911, we for the first time in our history had again a clerical government, and a bill was passed forbidding the dissemination of practical neomalthusian information publicly or when not asked for. This did not stop our work, but at the first elections that followed (last summer) the ministry was overthrown and now we have again a liberal government.

ance also with individual wishes, and last not least with the health and the energy of the parents, is freely preached in Holland as a common sense precaution, as a matter of course. So Holland is the best test of the results following when neomalthusianism is discussed freely and when the giving of information is not checked by law.

Intelligent and well to do people adopted the principle at once; the elite of the laboring class soon followed. But then came the danger that the unfit would multiply without limit and the fit would not multiply in the same ratio. Therefore the Neomalthusian League in Holland now doubles its efforts in order to deal with this transitional condition, and for twelve years our League has been working chiefly among the mass of laborers, where the information is also welcome as soon as it is brought within their reach. These last years even the very poor women begin to implore our assistance to obtain the appliances gratuitously.

It is our experience that information is asked, *first* for maintaining the standard of life in order to give to the children a good education and all necessities of life, *second* for sparing the health of the mother. Especially in the middle class and among the better paid laboring people, education of children is now careful and the bringing up joyous where formerly scarcity and anxiety reigned. Children are now a blessing, not a curse; they are welcome, or they are not born. Just as in former times I often noticed that death of infants was a relief and was acknowledged as such, so now parents are anxious for all that concerns the good health of the children. In this respect a reciprocal action may be observed: in families where children are carefully procreated they are reared carefully, and where children are carefully treated, they are carefully procreated.

So there are few countries where, proportional with the falling birth rate, the death rate of children in the first year of life has fallen so rapidly as in Holland, and our surplus of births over deaths is among the highest in the world, as Dr. C. V. Drysdale shows in his statistical diagrams.

Indeed parental prudence is no race-suicide, as could be presumed a priori. The statistical figures in Holland that cannot be denied prove that in practice neomalthusianism is a factor of race improvement. We see it in every case. Rich people that are too lazy, too luxurious, too selfish to want children, will die without leaving offspring. Poor people that are too miserable will also refuse to have children, since the laws forbid wage-work for children. Every mother that feels herself weak, exhausted, suffering, will prevent procreation. Only individuals that feel themselves happy, efficient, energetic, in good health, individuals endowed with a good humor and who love children heartily, only they will procreate, and that is all we want. It is conscious selection instead of brute natural selection. It is the same principle that all breeders of races in the animal kingdom and all gardeners have long since realized; there is no race improvement without limitation of numbers. Only in the human being it is the mother herself who is conscious if she feels well enough for this highest of all missions. How can any one imagine that ignorance and carelessness should be more propitious for the future of the race than intelligent consciousness!

The Neomalthusian League in Holland has worked now nearly 33 years in spreading knowledge. Mr. S. Van Houten, afterwards

Prime Minister, having prepared public opinion since 1877, the League was founded by Mr. C. V. Gerritsen, a well known business man and statesman, in Amsterdam in 1881, only four years after the inauguration of the first Neo-malthusian League in London, created by Dr. C. R. Drysdale, Sr.

This was a revival of public consciousness in sexual matters against ignorance and obscurantism. The first woman doctor in Holland, Dr. Aletta H. Jacobs in Amsterdam, was the first doctor to give information gratis to poor women. Our headquarters at The Hague and our subdivisions in all our greater towns are spreading theoretical leaflets and pamphlets; but the special pamphlet giving practical information in the prevention of conception, is only given to married people when asked. We are lecturing everywhere. But the essential missionary work is done privately and modestly, often unconsciously by showing the happy results in their own families, by the nearly 5,000 members of our League spread over the whole country, among whom are physicians, clergymen and teachers, etc. Every day information is asked by letters and still more by our printed postcards: all information is given cost-free and post-free. Almost all younger doctors and midwives are giving information, and are helping mothers in the cases when it is wanted on account of pathological indications. Moreover special nurses are instructed in helping poor women. Harmless preventive means are more and more taking the place of dangerous abortion. So, merely by our freedom of giving information, we have reached the desirable results proved most brilliantly by the statistical figures of our country.

Certainly there are abuses, but the abuses of knowledge are never so enormous as the abuses of ignorance. And hygiene is the highest form of morality.

THE PREVENTION OF CONCEPTION

By Clara G. Stillman.

An illuminating paper read at the recent Eugenics Congress ended with the sentence: "The great problem is not to bring better babies into the world, but to take care of such as come. The problem of the world is spoiled babies." And we may add that the solution of this problem will be materially advanced when we decide to bring less babies into the world.

Those who are convinced that the voluntary prevention of conception is a most important weapon in the modern fight with poverty, disease, and racial deterioration, will find their position only strengthened by a survey of their opponents' objections. These objections are mainly of three kinds—and might be classified as the pseudo-religious, the pseudo-moral and the pseudo-scientific, because all are based on conceptions which our present state of knowledge and social development have enabled us to outgrow. In the first we find the assertion that prevention is blasphemous, since it argues a lack of confidence in the wisdom of the Creator, who bade humanity: "Be fruitful and multiply." In the second, the fear that a knowledge of prevention will lessen the chastity of women, since they will no longer be deterred from illicit relations by fear of the consequences. In the third, the sinister prophecy that, with the methods of prevention a matter of common knowledge, the birth rate will decrease until humanity disappears from the earth. Or in some cases this latter objection is raised for some specific country from motives of patriotism, as for example in France to-day.

As for the first, some writer has already pointed out that the economic justification for the command to replenish the earth no longer obtains, since at the time when it was given there were only eight people in the world.

The question of the effect on woman's chastity may be taken more seriously. Undoubtedly absolute chastity in women will not be reckoned as high in the future as in the past. The ideal will be increasingly that of temperance rather than that of complete abstinence. But this change, which is already beginning to

be noticeable, will not depend on the prevention
of conception, but mainly on woman's changed
economic status, and our increased understand-
ing of sexual problems. Furthermore a chastity that depends for its existence on fear alone
is hardly a valuable moral asset. We may confidently expect that in the future economic independence, a knowledge of sex hygiene, and the
growing respect for her own individuality, will
keep woman from undesirable unions at least as
thoroly as she is kept from them to-day by
purely conventional considerations.

As for the idea that the birth rate will decrease until mankind dies out—this danger is a
purely imaginary one. The superior intelligence of man, by diminishing the risks of life,
has enabled him to cover the earth with billions
of his kind, and become its master, tho he is
the least fertile of all animals. Further it is
misleading to refer always to the falling birth
rate without relating it to the death rate. Not
a high birth rate but a low infant mortality is
a sign of vigor and high development.

These objections uniformly ignore present
conditions and the facts of organic and social
evolution which we now have at our command.

Social utility has come to be the measure of morality instead of the sanction of some arbitrary, external authority. Insofar as they are weighed in the balance of social utility and found wanting, the accepted religious and moral codes are being cast aside and the strong religious and ethical sentiments of mankind are for the first time finding their way into channels where their influence upon the world can be for good alone, since they will be based on actual knowledge and the passion for democracy in the place of superstition and the principle of submission.

If we then free our minds from old standards that are in no way related to modern life, and study impartially the effect that a general knowledge of preventive measures would have upon the social conditions of our day, we find first of all this situation:

Prevention of conception is already an accepted principle among the educated classes of every civilized country. According as the opposition of the law and public opinion are more or less stringent, it is practiced with more or less secrecy, but secret or open, the practice is here to stay and it is spreading. The fear of most of its opponents is therefore not nearly so much that the human race will become extinct, as that its best elements will gradually be replaced by the worst. At first glance this may seem plausible. Granting our opponents' premise temporarily, the conclusion is logically unavoidable that in order to restore a normal relation between the so-called more or less intelligent or desirable classes of society, we must put into the hands of all the methods of restricting their increase, now utilized only by the few. Far from coming to this conclusion, however, the opponents of so-called race-suicide strenuously oppose its spread, and instead of teaching prevention to the poor, preach procreation to the rich. As preaching has never yet availed to change the course of evolution, tho it may undoubtedly retard it, these people are simply stupidly and blindly intensifying the very condition they deplore.

Of course the validity of this argument rests on the assumptions: first, that the less fertile stocks must diminish, which as has been pointed out is quite contrary to fact; and second, that the higher and lower classes of society are high and low because of some inherent quality and not thru the powerful influence of environment. In this again they are utterly out of date since the determining part that poverty plays in every social problem, for years recognized only by Socialists, is slowly penetrating the public mind—as evidenced by the recent investigation connecting prostitution with low wages. Not only is poverty the fruitful cause of child labor, alcoholism, prostitution, criminality, defective mentality and degenerate physique, but these results become in their turn the causes of more poverty and more degeneration in an endless vicious circle. Whatever strikes a blow at poverty will strike a blow as well at these manifold forms of human misery.

It is from this point of view that the right to prevent conception appears not only morally justifiable, but a potent factor for moral regeneration. For each family only as many children as the mother can bear in health and the family income will permit of rearing in accordance with the highest existing standards of hygiene and education—this should be the first demand, so obviously rooted in common sense. The first consequence of feeling that we consciously call our children into being will be an increased sense of responsibility for each child that is born, rather than the helpless and hopeless fatalism that accepts them as sent by God and leaves it to Him to see them safely thru existence. God's success in this direction has not been brilliant, as witness our juvenile courts, our reform schools, our wayward and delinquent boys and girls, our spoiled babies by thousands and thousands that have become the problem of the world. With the knowledge of prevention common poverty, the wide-spread practice of abortion and that of infanticide will naturally disappear; another gain for health, morality and happiness. With less children among the poor, there is an increase of leisure for both mother and children, with the result that the standard of living rises. Children are kept and cared for at home and not dumped on the street to form part of the savage and bestial substratum of our civilization, and their young lives will not be blighted by premature toil under disgusting conditions.

Here is a woman, of whom I heard recently, who on the eighth anniversary of her marriage was expecting her eighth child. Now she lies in the hospital, having had several miscarriages since then. When her seventh child was born, they were so poor that she had to get up the next day. Her husband earned only $4.50 a week and her own mother was lying sick in the next room, where she remained helpless for nine months until she died. Another, with eleven children, thanked God when her drunken husband on one of his sprees walked off a pier into the East River. The assurance that she would never have to bear another child made the prospect of merely supporting the eleven she already had comparative Heaven. It sickens one to think what love and home means to these poor wretches and what life will do to their children, yet these cases are typical of thousands. The morality that accepts such conditions as normal and necessary must be abolished.

I hope to see the day when a poor woman can go to a health station to get instructions for preventing an undesired pregnancy as simply and naturally as she goes to-day to get a formula for modifying her baby's milk. Before this can be accomplished, however, much work will have to be done. Our physicians will have to throw overboard some of their professional ethics—wherever they conflict with social ethics

—and join with our sociologists and intelligent lay people in besieging the legislature with the demand to repeal the law which makes the giving of such information an offense punishable by five years' imprisonment. The suffragists in this state have been using this method of holding a hearing before a legislative committee every year for the past forty-five years. Their long patience is about to be rewarded, but when they began their cause was just about as unpopular as this is now.

We hear a great deal to-day about the unmaternal nature of the modern woman. But the accusation that the woman of to-day is less maternal than her greatgrandmother has nothing to substantiate it. We do not know how the woman of the past felt, since, in the first place, she was inarticulate; secondly, marriage was the only career open to her: and thirdly, marriage inevitably meant children. To look upon the large families of the past as expressions of woman's maternal sentiment is absurd. They were simply the expressions of her helplessness in the mechanical fulfillment of a duty imposed from without, a duty which often involved the sacrifice of her life. Our Colonial fathers, for instance, were quite in the habit of wearing out three or four wives in the process of building up those splendid, old-fashioned families of theirs. Some interesting figures on this subject are given by Wm. Hard in his book "The Women of To-morrow." Far from being a sign of ama-ternalism, as Ellen Key calls it, the movement to restrict the number of offspring results from the increased realization of the dignity and social importance of maternity. Its aim is to rescue motherhood from the degradation of being the plaything of passion, and raise it to the dignity of a science. Never before has there been such a high respect for motherhood as there is to-day.

If we pursue this tendency a little further, we find that it also fully justifies the woman who elects to have no children. If evolution means anything the instinct on which depends the future continuation of the race and all its past development cannot disappear. Whether one has children or not is a purely personal matter. Only after the child is born has society any rights, and then it has duties as well as rights. In the recognition of the individual nature of love and of the social nature of parenthood, the hitherto warring principles of individual happiness and social responsibility in the sexual sphere are at last beautifully harmonized—and this recognition represents the highest summit that our thought on the subject has yet reached, and the starting point for the morality of the future.

PREVENTION OF CONCEPTION AS A DUTY

By James F. Morton, Jr.

Prevention of conception is always a right, and very frequently a duty. I do not regard the question of limitation of offspring as primarily a quantitative one, but rather as fundamentally qualitative. In this, I part company most emphatically from Malthus and his earlier disciples. The pressure of population against subsistence is a theoretical possibility; but under conditions of freedom from land monopoly and of proper cultivation it could not menace any part of the earth for many generations. There is no actual case of over-population or even the near approach of the same. All apparent examples, like that of Ireland, when closely examined, turn out, as long since demonstrated by Henry George, to be the result of human blundering with regard to the use of natural resources and natural opportunities. With the lowering of the birthrate observable wherever general prosperity increases, it is probable that a natural barrier against excessive increase will be found amply operative under a better and more comfortable state of society.

The need of prevention of conception arises from quite a different cause, or rather from many causes entirely dissociated from the hypothetical approach of a time when standing-room on the earth shall be available for only a fraction of the population. It is a necessity because conditions favorable to sexual association are not uniformly favorable to procreation. While our theological moralistic friends are never weary of assuring us that Nature or what they call God created the sexual organs and sexual appetites for the sole purpose of guaranteeing survival and increase of the race, their unproven assertion is negatived by practical experience. No sex association without a subsequent childbirth means a maximum number of one association in two or three years during a fractional portion of the adult life of any man or woman. Even then, the outcome must be abnormally huge families, which, even if desirable, must be economically impossible to the average man and woman, or but from one to five or six sex acts in a whole lifetime. This is a situation which cannot be evaded. If the weak reply be made that attempts at procreation are not always successful, and that successive repetitions of the act are thus warranted and probable in many cases, before Nature's end is attained, but little is gained for the argument. The concession is too slight to alter the situation materially; and a premium is placed on natural barrenness, which of itself must tend to defeat the supposed plan of Nature. If the necessity of continence is to disappear after the childbearing stage is passed, the whole principle is abandoned; since if the one end of the sex act is procreation, persistence in it after the end has ceased to be possible must be as hostile to natural ethics as the use of scientific means to prevent conception.

The issue is a clearcut one. The enemies of prevention of conception must logically demand of all men and women a rigid sexual continence except on a few occasions, separated by long intervals. So far as appeasing the sexual urge is concerned, these few permitted occasions might as well be eliminated. If a sexual fast of several years is no hardship, the prolongation of such fast during the whole of life would be practically as easy. The few permitted tastes of the forbidden fruit are merely enough to whet the appetite, and to cause the deeper suffering from unsatisfied desire.* Yet the prohibition of anticonceptual methods involves nothing else. It is too late in the day to deny the existence and the imperative character of the sexual appetite. Theologians may regard it as a temptation of their friend the Devil; but science is compelled to recognize it as warp and woof o. our being. If Nature meant to render the sexual act just enticing enough to ensure the continuance of the race, she has been guilty of a grievous miscalculation, and has overshot the mark to an immeasurable extent. The most confirmed teleologist must admit this fact, or deny the universal testimony of history and everyday observation. The error of his deity must be counteracted in some way. If preventives be barred, what is the substitute?

One answer to the attempt to thwart a nat-

* In passing, it need only be suggested that a frequent result of such abnormal continence would be early impotence, involving a complete thwarting of Nature's presupposed purpose.

ural appetite is found in the institution known
as prostitution. Inevitable tho it is as a result
of an entire complex of conditions which will be
done away with, if at all, but slowly and in a
long period of time, sexual satisfaction for hire
rannot commend itself to the thoughtful mind
as ideal or in any way admirable as a finality.
It involves the setting apart of a fractional portion of one sex to relieve the surplus sexual needs
of a larger portion of the other sex.   The individuals thus set apart are sacrificed to a form
of specialization which practically destroys
their personal and social life in all other re-
spects. Moreover, the system is accompanied
by the spread of diseases of the most hideous and
deadly kind, which can be minimized but by no
means annihilated by precautions. These diseases reach far beyond the prostitute and her
patrons, and are speedily scattered among men,
women and children of all classes and degrees,
who are entirely innocent of voluntary contact
with the source of the infection. The complete
annulment of the use of preventives between lovers or married couples, and the consequent limitation of indulgence to the few occasions already mentioned, would inevitably create an in-

conceivably wider demand for relief thru other
channels; and prostitution, with its accompani-
ments of white slavery and venereal disease,
would thrive as never before, and would be assured of permanence and increase as an inevitable social institution.   Moreover, such relief
as it brings is but for one sex.   No outlet is
provided for strongly sexed, that is normal and
vigorously healthful women.   To meet their
need, the weak and waning institution of male
prostitution must be revived, and established in
full force.   Alternative to prostitution for both
sexes are only such avenues as self-abuse and
homosexualism, neither of which is likely to meet
the approval of our moralistic friends who demand the abandonment of preventives.   The
claim that no relief whatever will be found necessary is too absurd for further refutation.

Yet, tho the reactionary moralists have no
practical substitute to offer for scientific control of conception, they persist in denouncing
the application to this aspect of life of that cul-
tivated intelligence with which man prides himself on governing his other relations to the
world of nature.   Apart from the exploded tele-
ological argument, they rest their attacks

either on alleged ethical grounds founded on an antiquated theology, or on claims that preventives are artificial interferences with a natural process and that they are uniformly injurious. The theological argument is of no consequence to enlightened men and women. As to artificiality, no such thing exists. The human brain and all its products spring directly from nature, and result by logical sequences from her method of evolution. Prevention of conception is no more perniciously artificial than the eating of cooked food or the dwelling in elaborately constructed houses. The whole history of progress consists in the working over by human intelligence of the raw materials and crude activities of unintelligent nature. The charge of injuriousness, so often brought forward at an earlier period of the discussion of the subject, is not heard so often at the present day. That some methods of prevention have proved hurtful, and that others must be used with caution and under intelligent direction, need not trouble us greatly. The best modern scientific methods are free from this objection. Even at worst, the risk from an unsafe or ill applied method of prevention is but little compared to the certain

injury derived from excessive childbearing or
abnormally protracted continence. Excessive
procreation is pernicious to the woman; and its
result is the forcing into the world of a breed of
undesired and hence commonly undesirable children, condemned by both heredity and environment (even if prenatal influence prove not to be
scientifically maintainable) to wretched lives
and to careers often of positive evil to society.
Moreover, what is to be done with the by no
means negligible class of women who are physi-
ologically incapable of bearing children, and are
yet possessed of a full measure of normal sexual passion and deeply in love? What hope is
there for loving and passionate men and women,
who cannot beget or bear offspring without the
certainty of transmitting disease?

When driven from every other refuge, the
final cry of the conventionalist is that ability to
prevent conception will increase what he is
pleased to call immorality. The attitude of
mind which can frame such a proposition is
probably beyond the reach of reason, as it is
without sympathy for the inner needs of humanity. If the current dogmas of sexual ethics
rest on an unshakable foundation of natural

law, it is inconceivable that universal violation of them should be the inevitable result of the mere removal of a physical consequence. The average man or woman does not steal, simply because his hands are unchained, nor murder because a paving-stone lies ready to his hand. It is not the mere thought of material consequences that prevents individuals from the continual violation of their own codes. Higher ethical standards are reached by education, not by perpetual restraint of liberty.

As a matter of fact, the general knowledge of methods of preventing conception would not have the dire results so confidently predicted. The strength of the sexual appetite overrides the fear of consequences to-day; and those who from weakness of desire or from intensity of moral convictions find themselves able to resist its imperious call are not moved by a mere calculation of the chances of safety. The few who are at present continent from no other motive than fear of conception are in nearly all cases wearing out their lives in worse ways thru abnormal activities or thru a species of celibacy which hurts both themselves and the community worse than the gratification of their acute longings could possibly do.   At most, they are but a handful, in comparison with the other sufferers, both in and out of marriage, who are today the victims of unwelcome conception, freedom from which, without in the least increasing their sexual activities, would mean health and life and the more intelligent and careful breeding of offspring blessed and not cursed into the world.

PREVENTION A NECESSITY TO MARRIED LIFE

By Edwin C. Walker.

Among the many facts entirely ignored or only cursorily considered and then slightingly dismissed by the opponents of scientific prevention of conception, are these:

Late marriage is prevention of conception. It is a kind that inevitably and greatly augments the volume of involuntary sexual excitation in men and women, strongly tends to make early and occasional masturbation the habit of years or of life, leads surely to increased patronage of the prostitute and so more widely disseminates sexual diseases, spreads homosexuality, discourages normal and healthful sociability among men and women, driving members of each sex into one-sided associations that narrow the social outlook and harden the sympathies; and disturbs and wrecks the nervous systems of millions.

The "reformers" who seek the limitation of

the sexual association of a couple to the from
two to six times during life when offspring are
desired, also are propagandists of prevention of
conception, and of a particularly mischievous
kind, for to most of the evils flowing from late
marriage and which necessarily are concomi-
tants of this "reform," is to be added that of
sexual teasing, teasing of a peculiarly intimate
and trying and disintegrating nature. A man
and woman of strong or of even only moderate
sexual desires who love each other and who live
together must express their affection only by
tender words and caresses and kisses if they are
resolved to have no cohabitation except the very
few times when they think they are ready for
children. Such a loving and caressive association, stopping short always of its natural ter-
mination, leaves strained and aching testes and
ovaries, quivering and irritable nerves, all the
conditions that are the very seedbed of serious
neuroses, of bodily weakening and mental breaking. If it be said that those who adopt such a
regimen have the strength of will to endure all
consequences, it may be answered that the
strength of will which carried religious martyrs
to the stake did not prevent the flames perform-

ing the full ministry of fire upon their bodies. If it be further objected that this form of prevention will be chosen only by those whose sexuality is of very low voltage and who therefore will not be injuriously affected by the teasing of incomplete love-association, I retort that this amounts to a confession that only those whose power to help continue the race is very near the ebbing can escape the bad consequences of this kind of prevention of conception and that, no matter how great their intellectual powers may be, their racial strains soon must reach extinction.

The opponents of methods of limitation of the number of children which, while preventing the union of the spermatozoa and the ova, do not put upon the race the terrible burden of the evils I have named, and many more, usually conveniently forget that the alternative *practically* is not the discontinuance of non-procreative intercourse, but abortion, and that abortions will increase with the lessening of the inhibitory force of old superstitions, both without and within the pale of marriage, unless that evil is prevented by the "absorbent substitution of the opposite good," scientific prevention of

conception. As to those who lump prevention
and abortion together as equally evil, or as the
same thing, the less we say about their mentality and their ethics the less unparliamentary
we shall be. It has even been asserted, often,
that prevention is just as much "murder" as is
the destruction of a six-months embryo. Then,
of course, late marriage, association only when
children are desired, or the abstention from marriage of those who think themselves physically
or mentally unfit to procreate, is "murder."
This is the logical absurdity into which plunge
all who can not discriminate, who can not tell
likeness from unlikeness, who can not distin-
guish between prevention and abortion.

But I need not dwell here; others have covered
this part of the field fully and convincingly.
Suffice it to say, that the quickening conscience
of the race is revolting more and more against
the criminal childishness of the anti-naturalists;
the demand is growing that the banning of the
knowledge of harmless preventives shall cease,
that the forcing of the alternative of wholesale
infanticide, wholesale wrecking of the bodies and
torturing of the nerves of women, shall cease.
Every State or federal statute, every pronun-

ciamento of a church conclave, which places scientific prevention of conception in the category
with abortion is an insult to intelligence and a
crime against humanity.

INFANTICIDE, ABORTION, AND PREVENTION OF CONCEPTION

By L. Jacobi, M.D.

I

It is an established proposition that any species of plant or animal life, if allowed to multiply unchecked, would in no very long time overrun the entire surface of the globe. The multiplication of plants and animals takes place in a geometrical ratio. This sounds tame enough, but as soon as we attempt to realize the true meaning of such an increase, the statement becomes highly alarming. Much ingenious computation has been devoted to showing the result to be expected from unchecked reproduction. For example, the eggs of a single codfish, if allowed to mature thru several generations unmolested, would in three or four years fill the oceans with one solid mass. (The curious mathematician who performed this calculation, has left the resulting overflow out of considera-

tion.)   A plant yielding one hundred seeds an-
nually, would in ten years produce one hundred quintillions of adult plants. The ele-
phant, of all animals the slowest breeder, would
stock the entire world in several thousand years.
A single pair of guinea-pigs may produce 1000
in a single year (breeding begins at two months
of age).

To bring the marvelous natural process of
propagation vividly home to our limited imag-
ination, it may be said that the unhampered reproduction of any species would soon consume
the total quantity of matter contained in our so-
lar system!

However, all these interesting calculations
are made in the subjunctive mood. In reality,
no unmolested propagation ever takes place
long enough to reach such proportions.
Speaking of the codfish, we have no evidence of
any marked numerical increase, their number
probably remaining near a certain average thru
many generations. This means that only a
small minority of the innumerable codfish eggs
attain maturity, the vast remainder going to
waste. The apparent extravagance of nature
is nowhere more strikingly exemplified. Yet the

extravagance is only apparent. Millions of eggs are necessary in order that a few may develop into new individuals, for codfish-eggs have to run the gauntlet of infinite dangers from other creatures and from physical conditions. Vast numbers are doomed to destruction, a mere lucky handful emerging victorious from this so-called "struggle for existence." These few represent the "survival of the fittest," as the process has been aptly named by Herbert Spencer, a term now generally accepted.

In the words of John Fiske, "there is an unceasing struggle for life—a competition for the means of subsistence—going on among all plants and animals. In this struggle by far the greater number succumb without leaving offspring, but a few favored ones in each generation survive and propagate to their offspring the qualities by virtue of which they have survived." ("Cosmic Philosophy," Vol. II, Ch. X.)

And again: "Battles far more deadly than those of Gettysburg or Gravelotte have been incessantly waged on every square mile of the earth's life-bearing surface, since life first began. *It is only thus that the enormous in-*

crease of each species has been kept within bounds."

The human race is also subject to the same law of multiplication. Populations have been known to become doubled in 25 years, and, according to Euler's calculations, this result may be achieved under favorable conditions in half that period.

We may safely accept it as an axiom, that the multiplication of mankind is capable of rapidly outstripping the means of subsistence. According to Rev. Malthus, the famous author of the epoch-making "Essay on the Principle of Population," published in England in 1798, the means of subsistence increase in an arithmetical progression, while population grows in a geometrical progression, the latter quickly leaving the former far behind. Whether things can be reduced to such exact mathematical formulas or not, the essential truth inherent in the proposition of Rev. Malthus must be acknowledged as beyond the reach of doubt. And until the time arrives when man will be capable of utilizing the latent powers of his planet to an extent now undreamed, he must again and again be brought face to face with the problem of

keeping population within the limits of suste-
nance derived by human labor from Mother
Earth.

This tendency of population to tread on the
heels of production has from the earliest times
been the immediate cause of progress. "It produced," says Spencer in his "Principles of Biology," "the original diffusion of the race. It
compelled men to abandon predatory habits and
take to agriculture. It led to the clearing of
the earth's surface. It forced men into the social state; made social organization inevitable;
and has developed the social sentiments. It
has stimulated to progressive improvement in
production, and to increased skill and intelligence. It is daily thrusting us into closer contact and more mutually-dependent relation-
ships. And after having caused, as it ultimately must, the due peopling of the globe, and
the raising of its habitable parts into the highest state of culture—after having perfected all
processes for the satisfaction of human wants
—after having, at the same time, developed the
intellect into competence for its work and the
feelings into fitness for social life—after having
done all this, the pressure of population must

gradually approach to an end—an end, however, which it cannot absolutely reach."

While thus recognizing the beneficent rôle played by pressure of population in the evolution of mankind, we must not underestimate those forces which have always tended to antagonize the dangers of excessive propagation. It is not the latter alone that we have to credit with the blessings of civilization. Pressure of population alone, without the counter-pressure of antagonistic forces, would have produced no progress. Both were requisite to maintain a balance. Let us now dwell briefly on these checks to excessive multiplication.

In the past, pressure of population has ever been reduced and moderated by the wholesale destruction of human life in wars, epidemics, and periodical famines. Ravages by the larger beasts of prey have also contributed a small share (tigers in India, etc.).

Pestilential diseases, especially such as plague and small-pox, have repeatedly devastated the earth's population, and this far more thoroly and generally than any war. The death-dealing powers of Nature leave the enmity between man and man far behind. The great epidemic of "Black Death," which swept over Europe in the 14th century, carried off 25,000,000 lives, amounting to one quarter of the entire European population. During the Great Plague of London in the 17th century, 70,000 died. In America, as late as 1839, whole tribes of Indians have been wiped out by small-pox.

With the gradual elimination of wars and epidemics, and with the steady improvement in hygienic conditions, the pressure of overpopulation has shown a corresponding increase. Says a recent writer (Scott Nearing): "A continuance of the rate of increase in population which prevailed in the early 19th century would have resulted, in the near future of the Western World, in an overpopulation problem as serious as that now confronting China or India."

However, such a rate of increase has not continued, and to understand the reason we must turn our attention to a check on overpopulation not mentioned as yet, tho it is, perhaps, the most important of them all, according to high authority (Charles Darwin). This check, peculiar to man, supersedes the blind cosmic forces more and more as the human race advances.

It is the conscious effort to keep the number of newly born individuals within tolerable limits.

The earliest expedient resorted to by primitive peoples has been, naturally enough, the killing of infants at birth or shortly after. We find this method of infanticide still prevailing in many parts of the globe (it is common in Australia), and it may be safely inferred to have been very widely diffused in the past.

Infanticide is employed not only as a convenient means of regulating the growth of population, but serves also to determine its quality, for usually the weakest infants are put to death. Males being a more valuable asset in primitive society, it is ordinarily the females who are sacrificed. The custom of infanticide was at one time almost universal, and represents the earliest conscious effort at dealing a blow to a perilous rate of multiplication.

"The murder of infants," remarks Darwin in his "Descent of Man," "has prevailed on the largest scale thruout the world and has met with no reproach." And again: "Barbarians find it difficult to support themselves and their children, and it is a simple plan to kill their infants." M'Lennan in his "Primitive Marriage," also inclines to the view that these practices originated in the impossibility of supporting all the infants that are born.

True, some competent observers have attributed the fearfully common practice of infanticide partly to female vanity, the women wishing to avoid lactation in order to preserve their good figure, but this additional motive may be dismissed as negligible.

For the sake of completeness, other conscious checks to overpopulation may be fitly mentioned, for instance, licentiousness, encouraged here and there in the hope of keeping down the rate of increase. The same applies to homosexuality, occasionally sanctioned by various peoples for the purpose of retarding multiplication. Prostitution, also, has been credited by some authorities with a regulative function of this nature. Thus, G. de Molinari (La Viriculture) believes that prostitution has acted beneficially by neutralizing the excesses of the sexual impulse, indirectly suppressing the necessity of infanticide, and finally leading to the prohibition of that method.

In a very different way, prostitution has within recent years suppressed infanticide.

We are told, namely, that in a certain Chinese province it was customary for poor parents to kill some or all of the girls born to them, for they were too heavy a burden and brought no compensation.

Lately, however, the development of steamship lines along the coast has brought vice and prostitution along with it, and the Chinese girls can be sold profitably into brothels. Hence the killing of female infants has been abandoned in that province.

While it may be admitted that prostitution and other minor factors have not been without some influence on the custom of murdering infants, yet this influence has never been general or far-reaching enough to abolish infanticide. Quite another factor came into action before that institution was supplanted, as we shall presently see.

II

How long infanticide continued to be practiced, before it dawned on the primitive mind that it could be avoided by extinguishing the infant's life while yet in the mother's womb, is a matter of vague conjecture. Sooner or later,

however, the discovery was inevitable, and hence-
forth artificial abortion may be assumed to
have replaced gradually the custom of infanticide.

At first abortion was probably resorted to
only during the later stages of pregnancy, when
the expanding body of the mother betrayed her
condition even to the unobservant eye. The
initial stages are not likely to be recognized by
the savage, since intercourse begins early in
both sexes, and pregnancy often supervenes before menstruation has appeared, while later a
new impregnation may easily occur, and thus
the menstrual flow repeatedly anticipated and
kept in abeyance. When at last primitive man
had learned to recognize early pregnancy, efforts were probably made to interrupt it.

The substitution of abortion for infanticide
must be considered chronologically and ethically
a step in advance. The motives prompting
abortion are in general identical with the causes
of infant-murder. The deterring factors, such
as maternal love, or aversion to taking life,
which may have induced an occasional mother
to spare her child when infanticide was the custom, must have lost their influence with the ad-

vent of abortion. The latter could be invoked
without any such scruples and was no doubt a
welcome substitute for murder.

The extensive practice of artificial abortion
among the uncivilized and the semi-civilized
races ought to be a matter of astonishment to
those who blame civilization for all human ills,
and look backward upon "the state of nature"
as a paradise lost. The number of primitive
peoples resorting to artificial abortion is verily
legion.

Wherever it is employed, we usually find infanticide entirely abandoned, and this confirms
the conjecture indulged in above. Some peoples distinctly specify that abortion is permissible, while infanticide is punishable as murder. In fact, the majority of lower races look
leniently on artificial abortion, and even certain
civilized peoples sanction the practice. The
Turks, for example, allow it up to the fifth
month of pregnancy, as they consider the fetus
lifeless until that time.

It is interesting to take notice of the methods
employed by primitive races to procure abortion. Probably the oldest and most obvious
procedure consists in violent measures directed

against the abdomen of the pregnant woman. The "patient" lies down, and the wise old woman or the medicine-man kneels on the prostrate body, executes a dance on her stomach, kicks her, and maltreats her generally in various more or less ingenious ways, until certain symptoms make their appearance and testify to the success of the "operation."

With advancing knowledge of human anatomy and physiology, these crude measures become abandoned in favor of procedures directed against the fetus or the organs concerned with gestation. Special implements are designed for the purpose of puncturing the fetal membranes or dilating the *os uteri*, and these primitive inventions often show a high degree of ingenuity, besides bearing witness to a remarkable knowledge of local anatomy.

Medicinal remedies, too, have been very extensively administered for the purpose of producing abortion. These medicines were usually derived from vegetable sources, the occasionally great specific virtues were ascribed to certain disgusting substances of animal origin.

Making the necessary allowances for changes due to better knowledge of drugs and improved technique in manufacturing instruments, it must be confessed that in principle the crude efforts of lower races are not very different from the methods now in vogue among civilized peoples.

Of the latter it must be stated that abortion is universally practiced on a very extensive scale, and this condition of affairs dates back to ancient times. In Greece, Plato and Aristotle approved of artificial abortion, recommending its employment as early as possible. In Rome, abortion was very commonly procured, but the patriarchal law of the early Romans vested the right to produce abortion not in the mother, but in the father.

Abortion was unqualifiedly condemned only by the Christian Church, owing to certain theoretical notions, as Ellis says. Various penalties were gradually introduced, culminating in the declaration that artificial abortion is equivalent to murder. All these penalties and threats and exhortations have failed signally to hold the practice in check. "Abortion," says Havelock Ellis, "is exceedingly common in all civilized countries."

Nay, more than that, in recent years a strong

movement in support of the right to perform abortion has sprung up.

This movement appears to have originated in Italy, where Balestrini had published a learned and suggestive book on the subject, now recognized as a work of authority. His broad and humane ideas were received very warmly, especially by members of the legal profession, who rallied to his support.

Some years later a remarkable novel, called Le Droit d'Avortement, appeared in France. The author, Dr. Jean Darricarrère, advocated the thesis that a woman has the inalienable right to abortion.

In Russia, a similar view is presented by Artsibasheff in his now famous sensational novel Sanin. The protagonist cynically ridicules those who take abortion seriously. He considers the interruption of early pregnancy a matter of slight consequence, a mere interference with a "chemical reaction."

But it was in Germany that the new movement found its strongest advocates. Here a number of distinguished women have openly come forward in support of a prospective mother's right to abortion.

Countess Gisela Streitberg was the pioneer, with her book: "Das Recht zur Beseitigung Keimenden Lebens." She was followed by several capable feminine disciples, and soon a number of eminent lawyers joined the women in their fight against the legal restrictions placed upon abortion.

They argue that no laws are needed to protect the unborn child, since the natural maternal instincts are quite adequate, and will not be disobeyed in the absence of powerful and reasonable motives. When, however, such motives are present, no one has the right to force motherhood upon the unwilling woman.

That these ideas have not fallen upon unheeding ears, may be gathered from a resolution passed at the Woman's Congress in 1905, demanding that abortion should be declared punishable only when brought about by another person against the will of the pregnant woman.

"Alike on the side of practice and of theory," says Havelock Ellis, "a great change has taken place during recent years in the attitude towards abortion." There is even a noticeable tendency to shift all blame from the woman to her environment, and to look upon her not as an offender, but a victim of prejudice and circumstance.

[The author could have mentioned a number of other publications which indicate a radical change of attitude towards the question of abortion. In *belles lettres* the most important contribution is Brieux' famous play "Maternity"; this play, by the greatest living French dramatist, ought to be read by everybody. In Germany quite some literature has sprung up demanding a certain latitude for the pregnant woman in her decision as to whether or not she is willing to carry the fetus to full term. Among them we might mention "Das Keimende Leben" by Herbert Eulenberg which in the form of a lawyer's plea defending an accused woman abortionist demands the acquittal of the accused.

In the September 1912 issue of the *Critic and Guide* we referred to a memorial by a Berlin physician to the Penal Code Commission suggesting that every woman who has already had three children or any single girl who has been seduced or raped should have perfect legal right to have abortion induced on herself. But the most important contribution to the subject that has come to my notice is a work in two volumes by Dr. Eduard Ritter von Liszt, Royal Imperial District Judge in Vienna, entitled "Die Kriminelle Fruchtabtreibung." This is a work which discusses the subject in a calm, dispassionate, legal manner, and is worthy the careful attention of every earnest student of the subject. W. J. R.]

Admitting all these arguments, and giving due consideration to the exigencies of individual cases, we must, nevertheless, refuse to accept artificial abortion as a solution of the problem. Even where its employment may be condoned, it is a necessary evil at best, by no means an adequate and ethically sound remedy for overpopulation or for unwelcome pregnancy.

For abortion, while indubitably more humane than infanticide, is fraught with grave consequences to the woman. Entirely omitting the anxious question as to its status in regard to the unborn creature, and confining ourselves to cold utilitarian considerations, we cannot close our eyes to the misery, the suffering, the untimely deaths which so often follow in the wake of artificial abortion. Where life is not immediately forfeited, permanent disability frequently results. In many instances, serious operations are subsequently necessary, and not a few lives, spared at first, are snuffed out later as a direct penalty for violating nature's laws.

The waste of energy and the distress inflicted upon the woman herself and upon her family, not to mention the economic losses which weigh heavily on the less fortunate, are in themselves arguments against abortion, more powerful and eloquent than any rhetoric.

It would be sad indeed, were the human race condemned forever to invoke the aid of this gory expedient in its struggle against excessive multiplication. Fortunately, however, the outlook is not so bleak. There is another resource, certain to become widely diffused, and destined to supplant artificial abortion, even as abortion suppressed infanticide.

III

It may be conjectured that interruption of pregnancy during the later months was gradually abandoned in favor of earlier interruption, and the steadily receding time of interference must have finally suggested a desire to avert pregnancy altogether. Presently some means was devised to accomplish this purpose, and humanity witnessed the origin of a new departure in dealing with the ubiquitous problem of overpopulation. For a long time preventive attempts must have been tentative and sporadic, the older expedient of abortion continuing to exist side by side with the new method, and slowly yielding ground to its encroachments. It is only in comparatively recent times that we find abortion rapidly receding before measures employed to prevent conception in cases where pregnancy is unwelcome.

This *prophylaxis of conception*, as I prefer to call it (meaning in Greek: guarding against or warding off), was known and occasionally employed in antiquity, as may be gathered from a familiar passage in Genesis (xxxviii): And Judah said unto Onan, Go in unto thy brother's wife, and marry her, and raise up seed to thy brother. And Onan knew that the seed should not be his; and it came to pass, when he went in unto his brother's wife, that he spilled *it* on the ground, lest that he should give seed to his brother." In modern terms, Onan sought to guard against conception by practicing *coitus interruptus*. Erroneously, however, his name has become associated with masturbation ("onanism").

The ancient Greeks, too, had remedies called Atokia, which prevented (or were supposed to prevent) conception, and were distinguished from Phthoria, or remedies producing abortion. In early Roman days, Soranus, the greatest obstetrician of antiquity, advocated prevention of conception as a substitute for abortion, with the dangers of which he was familiar.

Nevertheless, it is only in modern times that prophylaxis of conception has come to be widely employed, and this movement for the control of procreation may be said to date from Malthus' famous "Essay on Population" (1798). In this book, as we have already indicated, the author assumes that propagation of the human race takes place in a geometrical progression, while the means of subsistence can be augmented much more slowly, corresponding to an arithmetical progression. As a result, starvation is ever threatening mankind, and can be averted only by a judicious control of propagation. Malthus was a clergyman, and the remedy he proposed consisted in "self-control," that is, he counseled judicious abstinence from sexual intercourse as the best preventive measure. He believed that the power of self-control increased *pari passu* with civilization, and would enable people to refrain altogether from marital pleasures when such restraint was demanded in the interest of the race.

Without denying these assertions some semblance of truth, we are compelled to say that the Reverend Malthus failed signally in his estimate of the influence wielded by the reproductive instinct. He reckoned without his host, and suggested a cure which was worse than the disease. His naïvely-sincere attitude brought him an abundance of undeserved ridicule, and his book is nowadays mentioned with an indulgent smile.

He had not lived and labored in vain, however. His ideas were adopted by several followers, who recognized the truth inherent in his statements, while they cast about for more practicable preventive measures than mere self-control.

The pioneer in advocating these so-called Neo-malthusian methods was James Mill, father of John Stuart Mill. He aired his views very cautiously in an article written in 1818 for the

Encyclopedia Britannica. Four years later,
his friend Francis Place, wrote as follows on the
subject: "If it were once clearly understood
that it was not disreputable for married persons
to avail themselves of such precautionary means
as would, without being injurious to health, or
destructive of female delicacy, prevent conception, a sufficient check might at once be given to
the increase of population beyond the means of
subsistence. The course recommended will, I
am freely persuaded, at some period be pursued
by the people even if left to themselves."

These prophetic words were realized in another half-century and now prevention of conception is affecting the birth-rate of all civilized
countries. There are societies and periodicals
in all civilized languages, devoted to the propagation of Neo-malthusian principles.

"It is no longer permissible," says Havelock
Ellis, "to discuss the validity of the control of
procreation, for it is an accomplished fact and
has become a part of our modern morality."

The same view is taken by Sidney Webb
(*Pop. Science Monthly*, 1906, p. 526): "If a
course of conduct is habitually and deliberately
pursued by vast multitudes of otherwise well-

conducted people, forming probably a majority of the whole educated class of the nation, we must assume that it does not conflict with their actual code of morality."

This widespread resort to prophylaxis of conception finds its expression in the decline of the birth-rate, and eminent authorities can be quoted to show that this decline must be attributed to *voluntary intervention*.

Says Scott Nearing, in a paper on Race Suicide vs. Overpopulation (1911): "Any *conscious* restriction in the birth-rate is popularly referred to as race-suicide. It is in this sense that Roosevelt employed the term. The prevalence of a conscious restriction in the birth-rate on the part of the vast majority of American families has been established beyond question. Until 1850 any great increase in population was prevented by a high death rate. In the succeeding century, as a result of science and sanitation, the death rate was gradually reduced, and an overwhelming increase in population was prevented in only one way—by decreasing the birth-rate. The decline in the birth-rate therefore saved the modern civilized world from over-population and economic dis-

aster. An equilibrium of population has been
reëstablished thru the saving grace of the decrease in the birth-rate, commonly called "race
suicide."

Prof. H. W. Conn likewise considers the diminishing birth-rate *voluntary:* "My own belief
is that this is the greatest factor in the diminishing size of families. Indeed, I should rather
be inclined to believe that if this factor could
be removed, we should find the race practically
as fertile as in previous generations."

According to Dr. John S. Billings (*Forum,*
1893), one of the chief causes of the diminishing birth-rate is the "diffusion of information
with regard to the subject of generation by
means of popular and school treatises on physiology and hygiene, which diffusion began between 30 and 40 years ago. Girls of 20 years
of age at the present day know much more
about anatomy and physiology than did their
grandmothers at the same age, and the married women are much better informed as to the
means by which the number of children may be
limited than were those of 30 years ago."

Prof. Chas. F. Emerick, after a study of this
subject, sums up as follows: "Our conclusion is

that the diminishing birth-rate is primarily volitional, and that the various factors which make for involuntary sterility are of minor importance." And he rightly adds that "the weight of well-defined opinion supports the view that the decline of the birth rate is volitional."

In his "Essentials of Economic Theory," Clark says: "There are measures not here to be named in detail, which keep down the number of births. By strength and also by weakness, by virtue and also by vice, is the economic mandate which limits the rate of growth of population carried out."

These opinions may be accepted as conclusive evidence of the frequency and universality with which prophylaxis of conception is practiced by modern civilized peoples. If additional proof is demanded, it may be found in the attitude of the Church towards this practice. "The Church," says Ellis, "always alive to sexual questions, has realized the importance of the modern movement and has adapted herself to it, by proclaiming to her more ignorant children that incomplete intercourse is a deadly sin, while refraining from making inquiries into this matter among her more educated members." He concludes that "the adoption of preventive methods of conception follows progress and civilization, and the general practice of such methods, by Catholics and non-Catholics, is merely a matter of time."

Passing over this familiar reactionary attitude of the Christian Church, let us inquire how the modern movement is viewed by philanthropists, sociologists, physicians, and thinking people generally. Here are a few representative voices.

Prof. Edward A. Ross pleads for education along the lines of birth-restriction: "Education is what is needed—education directed against the old idea that it is the woman's duty to bring as many children into the world as possible in the belief that God will look after these children when they are brought here. Neither do I believe in the restriction of marriage save in the case of physical or mental defectives. Marriage is the normal state for all, whether poor or rich. But marriage, with poverty as a condition, should necessarily restrict the number of children.

"What I stand for is the national need for a

more perfect knowledge of parental responsibility among all classes of our people."

Dr. William J. Robinson writes emphatically as follows: "There is no single measure that would so positively, so immediately contribute towards the happiness and progress of the human race as teaching the people the proper means of prevention of conception. This has been my sincerest and deepest conviction since I have learned to think rationally. It is the sincere and deep conviction of thousands of others, but they are too cowardly to express it in public."

Another physician, Dr. William L. Holt, says: "Conscious and limited procreation is dictated by love and intelligence; it improves the race. Unconscious, irresponsible procreation produces domestic misery and half-starved children."

The opinion of women themselves on this subject is naturally very valuable: Here is what Mrs. Helen La Reine Baker has written: "There are already too many children in the world. What we want now is quality and not quantity. Parents should be taught the responsibility of bringing children into the world.

When the birth-rate will decrease, we shall have a better and stronger race."

H. G. Wells, the brilliant English writer, is not alarmed by the continued fall in the birth-rate in America and in Europe. He pleads for "more temperate and better controlled procreation."

These quotations could be multiplied indefinitely. Let one more reference suffice. Thruout Herbert Spencer's works there are scattered pithy expressions of his views on our subject. A few extracts may fitly conclude our survey of authoritative opinion.

Speaking, in the "Principles of Biology," of human population in the Future, he says: "In proportion as the emotional nature becomes more evolved, and there grows up a higher sense of parental responsibility, the begetting of children that cannot be properly reared will be universally held intolerable."

And again, in the "Principles of Ethics": "If, however, improvident marriages are to be reprobated—if to bring children into the world when there will probably be no means of maintaining any, is a course calling for condemnation; then there must be condemnation for those who bring many children into the world when they have means of properly rearing only a few. Improvidence after marriage cannot be considered right, if improvidence before marriage is considered wrong."

Elsewhere in the same work we read: "While the rate of multiplication continues so to exceed the rate of mortality as to cause pressure on the means of subsistence, there must continue to result much unhappiness; either from balked affections or from overwork and stinted means. Only as fast as fertility diminishes, which we have seen it must do along with further mental development, can there go on such diminution of the labors required for efficiently supporting self and family, that they will not constitute a displeasurable tax on the energies." In the meantime, while waiting for the adequate decrease of fertility to take place naturally, Spencer is in favor of prevention of conception, as will be evident from the following parenthetical phrase from a sentence occurring in his Ethics: "When the pressure of population has been rendered small—*proximately by prudential restraints*, and ultimately by decrease of fertility," etc.

In the "Principles of Ethics" there is also this passage: "While the struggle for existence among men has to be carried on with an intensity like that which now exists, the quantity of suffering to be borne by the majority must remain great. This struggle for existence must continue to be thus intense so long as the rate of multiplication continues greatly in excess of the rate of mortality. Only in proportion as the production of new individuals ceases to go on so greatly in excess of the disappearance of individuals by death, can there be a diminution of the pressure upon the means of subsistence, and a diminution of the strain and the accompanying pains that arise more or less to all, and in a greater degree to the inferior."

In his last book, "Facts and Comments," written, as he tells us in his letters, at the rate of ten lines per day, he says emphatically (Chapter "Some Regrets"): "I detest that conception of social progress which presents as its aim, increase of population, growth of wealth, spread of commerce. In the politico-economic ideal of human existence there is contemplated quantity only and not quality. Instead of an immense amount of life of low type I would far sooner

see half the amount of life of a high type. . . .
Increase in the swarms of people whose existence is subordinated to material development is
rather to be lamented than be rejoiced over."

IV

It is evident that prevention of conception is
not a remedy for overpopulation only, but a
powerful factor in improving the quality of the
race.   We may here appropriately consider the
various groups of cases in which conception is
best avoided.

The least objectionable are the strictly medical indications.   There are many pathological
conditions in which pregnancy and childbirth
are equivalent to serious impairment and short-
ening of life, or even to death.   There is no
room for difference of opinion when a woman is
afflicted with advanced tuberculosis, organic
heart-disease, grave changes in the kidneys, etc.
Here the law permits even the use of artificial
abortion when pregnancy has supervened, and
no one will hesitate to advise the patient to
avoid becoming pregnant altogether.   We have
no right to demand the sacrifice of the mother's
life for the sake of the progeny.   Here pro-

phylaxis of conception is undertaken in the interest of the woman.

A different indication is furnished by those diseases or hereditary defects of the parents which are likely to be transmitted to their offspring. Syphilis, insanity, degeneracy, and grave moral taints belong to the group. Here it is clearly a service to the race to desist from propagating imbeciles, lunatics and criminals. This might be called the eugenic indication for prophylaxis of conception, and the law, again, has recognized it. In some States there is a legal provision demanding the sterilization of confirmed or habitual criminals. Prevention of propagation is thus assured from the outset.

After the medical and the eugenic indications, comes the economic one. This usually meets with opposition from certain quarters, yet no valid argument can be presented against it. It benefits the parents, it is decidedly beneficial to society, and it is even merciful toward the unborn and unconceived creature, which is frequently saved from a life of misery. If we have no right to demand a sacrifice of the mother for the sake of the child, neither have we the right to demand sacrifices which, tho stopping short of being immediately fatal, nevertheless shorten and cripple the woman's life.

Finally, there are numerous and varied cases, when a woman, having conceived, will seek to interrupt pregnancy at any price. Here, if anywhere, prevention is preferable to "cure."

Such are the principal cases and conditions calling for prophylaxis of conception, and when this method of dealing with them becomes generally adopted, then will commence the period of seven lean years for all those who now thrive by interrupting undesirable pregnancy. Who will deny that much unhappiness and misery will thus be averted, and that society will gain incalculably in consequence?

Finally, prophylaxis of conception cannot fail to exert an indirect influence on our current sex morality. By conferring upon the woman immunity from the most dreaded sequel of illicit indulgence, it will undoubtedly tend to equalize the conduct of both sexes when confronted by temptation, and by generally facilitating marriage, it is bound to contribute toward the establishment of more hygienic sex relations, which, again, must redound to the benefit of society at large.

LET ME BE CREATED IN LOVE

By James P. Warbasse, M.D.

A proposition that would seem scarcely to need defense is that the uncreated child should not force itself upon parents who do not want it. It is so apt to find itself in an uncongenial atmosphere that three are caused to suffer where two were happy before.

There was a time, in the days of constant warfare, with its frightful mortality, and in the days of slow industry, with its meager productivity, that people and more people were needed to fight and toil and kill and die. But the machine, the conquest of disease, and the passing of the superstitions which glorified the crimes of war, all prompt mankind to produce more people not for the sake of the numbers alone. Only the capitalist, with his hunger for profits, and the priest with his hunger for sheep to enlarge his fold, now cry out: "Give us more people, for upon their backs we ride to glory."

But to breed people, to be thrown into the

hopper to be ground into profits, and to bring forth sinners, to be saved for the glory of the saviors, is not so highly esteemed a human function as it erstwhile was.

Were the unconceived child to speak perhaps it might say: "Let me be created in love and born only as a gift to parents whose hands are held out with loving welcome to receive me. Spare me from the hostile frown of my creators." A babe is so important a thing that it is deserving only of loving parents; and parents and lovers are so important that to mar their union by an unwelcome child is to threaten both parenthood and sexual love.

AFTERWORD TO THE EIGHTH EDITION

The Birth Control Movement has made wonderful progress since the first edition of this book made its appearance. And I cannot but believe that the change of public opinion is due to some extent to the arguments presented in its pages.

The book has been placed in the hands of a great number of legislators, senators, congressmen, judges, lawyers, clergymen, editors, charity organizers and social workers. And we know that while anathematized by some, it has moulded the opinions of thousands and thousands of influential people. The most conservative body in any community is the judiciary. But even the judicial citadel has been penetrated, and we have now judges expressing their sympathy with the Birth Control Movement openly from the bench. On September 13th of this year Judge Charles A. Dudley of Des Moines, Iowa, openly advised a couple who had nine children whom they could not support to acquaint themselves with birth-control methods. And he gave his opinion that "Theodore Roosevelt with his anti-race suicide talks has done more harm to this country than any other living man." And only the other day (October 12, 1916) a New York judge, William Henry Wadhams of the Court of General Sessions, refused to sentence a woman who was convicted for stealing money in order to feed her children: he stated that as long as it was illegal to teach the poor how to control the number of their offspring, it was not fair to send their parents to prison because they committed illegal acts in order to feed their starving progeny. Future generations, he said, will look aghast at our ignorance and at our laws.

When judges are beginning to show *publicly* their sympathy with the Birth Control propaganda, and point out the ridiculousness and the brutality of our prevention of conception laws, we may well say that the world does move.

And I might say that Chapters 28 and 29, which have annoyed so many impatient people, causing them to storm and to swear, are the most eloquent chapters in the book, and have proved the most efficient weapon in stimulating the people's indignation against our unjust laws. One judge and one Governor of a State wrote to me that it was those pages that, more than anything else, made them see the absurdity of our laws and induced them to work quietly for their abrogation, or to see to it at least that they became a dead letter on our statute books.

I will leave these two chapters the way they are for a little while longer. Perhaps in the tenth or fifteenth edition I will be able to be a little more explicit and go somewhat more into detail of the *methods* of birth control than I can at the present time.

DR. DRYSDALE'S OPINION OF THIS BOOK

There is no one who can put the case for family limitation by contraceptive methods more satisfactorily for the general reader than Dr. William J. Robinson, and his latest book on the subject must have been welcomed by very many thousands of readers, albeit that he has been obliged by the Comstock censorship to stop short at the vital point—the giving of the necessary information. Dr. Robinson has many qualifications which make him especially fitted to inspire confidence in this domain. His experience as a physician specialising in the treatment of sexual diseases has brought him into intimate contact with the hygienic evils of large families on the one hand, and those arising from prostitution, sexual abstinence, abortion, and unskilled attempts at prevention on the other. His sympathy with socialistic and other "advanced" views is tempered with an eminently sane and practical outlook upon things as they are, and no one reading his powerful defence and advocacy of artificial birth-control can feel for one moment that he is labouring under the obsession of an enthusiast. What the ordinary man and woman wants to know is as to whether family limitation is justifiable, first, for themselves and their children; second, for the State; whether contraceptive devices are bad for the health; whether they lead to early loss of sex power or to sterility; whether it is better to preach sex abstinence, etc. To all these questions, and to many others, Dr. Robinson's book gives direct and convincing answers, and even though a few of them depend principally on his own *ipsi dixit*, no one can doubt from his experience and the tenor of his writing that he is perfectly justified in his conclusions. . . .

From cover to cover, Dr. Robinson's book is full of interest, and if he were only able to fill in the blank chapters, it would contain practically everything which the ordinary man and woman wants to know. It is earnestly to be hoped that before many months are past the American public will see to it that Dr. Robinson is able to complete his valuable work.

DR. C. V. DRYSDALE, in *The Malthusian.*

GENIUS AND BIRTH CONTROL.

It is jolly to have the Catholic clergy join the discussion of Birth Control. Whether *pro* or *con* does not matter, in fact, their opposition is apt to do more good than their support. When Archbishop Hayes excoriates birth control as immoral, unnatural and what not, he is within his proper sphere. He has a right to his opinions, which are merely opinions based on sentiment and faith. But in an attempt to enter the arena of science and facts, he should be more careful, because there a very humble citizen may discredit his arguments—in one round—or in one paragraph.

The good Archbishop says: "Physicians have found that on the average, successive children in a family are stronger and healthier up to the fifth and sixth in succession, and that those marked with special genius are often born after the fifth in the family." He further states: "It has been suggested that one of the reasons for the lack of genius in our day is that we are not getting the ends of the families."

Both these statements are as contrary to fact as superstition is contrary to science. In my debate with the Reverend Richard H. Tierney, editor of "America, the national Catholic weekly," I discussed that very point from every angle, and if the Archbishop had read my paper, which he should have done before joining in a discussion of the subject of birth control, he would not have made the statements he has. In that paper, (see "Small or Large Families," published by The Critic and Guide Co.) I demonstrated beyond the possibility of contradiction that the claims of the Birth Control opponents that the first and second children are inferior, was altogether false and that the contrary was true.

For instance, I showed that almost all the great men, in fact, the world's greatest men in every domain of science and the arts, were first children. Lord Byron, John Keats, Alexander Dumas, both father and son, Robert Louis Stevenson, Emile Zola, Goethe, Friedrich von Schiller, Francis Bacon, William Shakespeare, Robert Burns, Thomas Carlyle, Heinrich Heine, Herbert Spencer, Baruch Spinoza, Immanuel Kant, Arthur Schopenhauer, Samuel Johnson, Edward Gibbon, Cardinal Newman, John Ruskin, Petrarch, Boccaccio, Leonardo da Vinci, Henrik Ibsen, Jean Racine, Johannes Kepler, Karl von Linne, Isaac Newton, William Harvey, Adam Smith, John Stuart Mill, Leon Gambetta, Martin Luther, Charlemagne—all were first children. And last, but not least, George Washington was his mother's first child.

And here are a few names of great men who were second children: Pope Leo XIII, Albrecht Durer, Balzac, Jean Jacques Rousseau, Ralph Waldo Emerson, Mozart, Johann Sebastian Bach, Ernest Renan, Leo Tolstoy, Charles Dickens, Walt Whitman, Edwin Booth, Abraham Lincoln, Frederick the Great, Alexander von Humboldt, Camille Cavour, Prince Bismark, William Pitt. The good Bishop should study the histories of great men.

But it is not only mentally and spiritually that we find the greatest men among the first children; even physically the same holds good. In *The American Journal of Heredity*, September 1916, there appeared a paper by the editor, who investigated the records of 802 cases of individuals, most of whom were *over ninety* years of age, only a few being included between eighty and ninety. It was found that the greatest percentage among them were first born children!! Namely, the first born constituted 27 per cent., the second born, 15 per cent., third, fourth and fifth, 13 per cent., the rest ranging between 7 and 11 per cent. As I stated in the above referred to paper, eight hundred people is not perhaps a very large number from which to draw final conclusions.

But the figures of the first-born nonagerians and centenarians certainly go at least to show the falsity of the claims of our theological and non-theological pseudo-eugenists that first-born children are weaker and shorter lived than the later born.

"Confronted with such social problems as the gangster, the drug addict, girl traffic and the like, our welfare agencies, public and private, are sadly depressed to see tolerated for a moment the danger of spreading among the immoral the lure of passion and the irresponsibility lurking in the present Birth Control advocacy, that aims at making the marriage relation more lustful and less fruitful."

If this paragraph had not been written by an archbishop I should have some fun with it, showing its utter absurdity. But as it is, may I ask the Archbishop where the gangster, the drug addict and the street-walker come from principally? If he will investigate the subject in an unbiased spirit, he will find that they come principally and primarily from families that breed like rabbits, where the children are so numerous that the parents are unable to give them the proper physical and spiritual education.

If the good Archbishop really wants to see the disappearance of the gangster, the drug addict, and the prostitute, he could do nothing better, nothing more effective, than to tell his priests to instruct the married women-members of his church, particularly the poor, in the proper use of prevenceptives. I will undertake to instruct any woman coming with a letter from a priest in the proper use of prevenceptives and without the cost of a single penny.

Postscript: *A Little Secret.*

All the anathemas of the church, all the persecutions, all the arrests, will not stop the spread of the birth control movement. I am surprised that the Catholic church, which is generally pretty clever in noticing the trend of the times, does not see this. The cat is out of the bag and all the forces in the world cannot put it back again. The opposition may temporarily obstruct the progress of the birth control movement, but kill it, it cannot. In fact, it is a question whether it can even obstruct it. Only too often opposition to a movement increases its momentum. It seems to be so in the present case.—*From* THE CRITIC AND GUIDE, *January, 1922.*